SONGS OF
THE BRITISH
MUSIC HALL

Published by

Wise Publications

14-15 Berners Street, London W1T 3LJ, UK.

Exclusive Distributors:

Music Sales Limited

Distribution Centre, Newmarket Road, Bury St Edmunds, Suffolk IP33 3YB, UK.

Music Sales Corporation

180 Madison Avenue, 24th Floor, New York NY 10016, USA.

Music Sales Pty Limited

Units 3-4, 17 Willfox Street, Condell Park, NSW 2200, Australia.

Order No. AM1004234

ISBN: 978-1-78038-390-3

This book © Copyright 2013 Wise Publications, a division of Music Sales Limited.

Written by Graham Vickers
Design by Don Wise & Company/Luisa Lowrie
Cover design by Don Wise

Music engravings by Paul Ewers Music Design
Edited by Toby Knowles
Picture research by Jacqui Black
Printed in the EU

SONGS OF

THE BRITISH
MUSIC HALL

By Graham Vickers

Wise Publications
part of The Music Sales Group

London / New York / Paris / Sydney / Copenhagen / Berlin / Madrid / Hong Kong / Tokyo

CONTENTS

"Born on a Friday."

LIST OF SONGS

FOREWORD

The Music Hall's breeding ground had been the London pleasure gardens that had once hosted a range of entertainments and diversions in outdoor settings of fanciful charm. Such places often boasted walkways, maze-like gardens, pavilions and architectural curiosities. Vauxhall Gardens near the south bank of the Thames was the most famous but by no means the only British example. The Ranelagh Gardens and Cremorne Gardens, both in Chelsea, also housed entertainment venues as did two others located in Lambeth and Marylebone. The expansion of London and the development that came with it ate up most of these gardens from the middle of the 19th century onwards, and as a result the entertainment acts they once hosted were obliged to move to new homes. Indoor halls soon became the natural option for increasing numbers of displaced performers, although in some cases such moves predated the closure of the gardens. This shift marked the informal birth of the Music Hall.

Today a first-hand appreciation of the British Music Hall is scarcely a living memory for anyone. It has receded into history and can now be conjured only through sound recordings, posters and the video or audio reminiscences of those who remembered going to the Music Hall or at one time might even have been performers themselves. Of course, the songs of the Music Hall live on—tuneful, bracing and often very clever commentaries of 80 or so years of British working-class manners and mores, hopes and dreams. Some of the very best of those songs have been collected in this book.

Music Hall started in the mid-1850s and flourished up to World War II before finally drifting into a post-war period of decline in the face of expanding rival entertainments such as the cinema, the radio and gramophone records.

The new venues were often pub saloon bars big enough to accommodate not just singing, but also dancing, drama and comedy. The trailblazer was The Grecian Saloon, established in 1825 at The Eagle—a former tea-garden—in north London. Soon promoted from 'Saloon' to 'Theatre', the Grecian was where precocious Marie Lloyd made her debut at the age of 14 in 1884. After a vigorous infancy in the saloons of the mid-19th century, Music Hall soon expanded into bigger theatrical venues. It was to last for less than a century. In his 1957 play *The Entertainer,* John Osborne already mourned its death:

'Some of the heart of England has gone…something that once belonged to everyone…truly a folk art.' One of Music Hall's latter-day heroes, Max Miller, survived into the 1960s, and it was said by many—including Miller himself—that his passing would mark the end of the Music Hall. In truth, rather like Dorothy Parker who inconveniently outlived her 1930s Manhattan glory days to become an irascible recluse in the alien 1960s, Miller survived well beyond the phenomenon with which the public associated him. Even that association, much promoted by Miller himself, was questionable because he had risen to national fame between the wars as a revue and variety performer rather than as a dyed-in-the-wool Music Hall entertainer. Variety theatres had started to spring up at the end of the 19th century, seeking to rehouse the Music Hall in more sophisticated and luxurious theatrical settings. The original halls had always looked like the adapted pub annexes or tearooms they had previously been, but variety theatres marked a shift of power and stewardship to professional theatre owners, who would replace pub-style tables and chairs with conventional audience seating in drinks-free auditoriums. The variety theatre bill would also seek to attract a wider audience and its buildings would be grander and, increasingly, lit by electricity. The London Pavilion, whose neo-classical exterior still exists in Piccadilly Circus, set the grand tone, and the Coliseum in St Martin's Lane and the Palladium in Argyll Street soon followed. London's licensing body of the time, the London County Council, began to take more notice of the content of theatrical performances and the

Music Hall came of age—or, conversely, started to become sanitised—when saucy Marie Lloyd was pointedly excluded from the first ever Royal Variety Performance held at the Palace Theatre at Cambridge Circus in 1912. It was in this slightly more genteel world of variety that Max Miller found the winning formula for his solo front-of-cloth act in 1930 at the London Palladium. It was a far cry from the spit and sawdust of the halls which Miller had only very briefly essayed in 1919, and so his reputation for blue material should always be seen in the context of his variety performances. Eventually Max Miller, Music Hall's self-appointed last man standing, proved that he had not lost his sense of timing when he died in 1963, the same year that two other portentous events took place. The Beatles recorded their debut album *Please Please Me*; and one of London's most famous Music Hall theatres—the Metropolitan in Paddington—was unceremoniously demolished immediately after renting itself out as a location for the filming of a tawdry horror film. These were surely the belated last rites for Music Hall, which had in reality expired well over a decade before, after a long illness.

This book presents the words and music of 50 songs from its heyday. A few of these songs are so famous that they seem to be imperishable and people born more than a century after they were written often seem know the tune and the chorus if nothing more. In such cases folk art has become part of the folk memory. Other songs will be less familiar, but not necessarily for reasons of quality since even the best song needed a popular performer to make it famous in the first place. Most of these numbers belong to a tradition of song writing in which the lyricist was not afraid to write many verses or to use language in an imaginative and sometimes convoluted way, even for the most accessible and broad topics. A case in point is lyricist Edgar Bateman's brilliantly sustained conceit 'If It Wasn't For The 'Ouses In Between' about an East End costermonger's self-deluding notion that his cramped urban house and backyard have rural potential and command sweeping views across London to the greenery beyond. Spoken sections were also sometimes introduced between verses, creating a hybrid form of song and patter. This is not entirely surprising—in the age of Gilbert and Sullivan the practice of matching lyrical tunes to artfully witty lyrics in the context of an operetta was a fully understood convention. There was no reason not to apply similar methods to lowbrow songs meant for audiences who would never set foot in D'Oyly Carte's Savoy Theatre. Whether a more down-to-earth Music Hall song's theme was about social pretension ('Burlington Bertie From Bow'), sexual body language ('Every Little Movement') or that poor East End costermonger longing for the bucolic life, no lyricist seemed afraid of using clever writing, capable of painting a vivid and detailed picture of a song's central comic notion. Significantly, most Music Hall songs were, to some degree, comic. Even the most solemn-sounding titles were usually undercut by a lyric that revealed itself to be satirical or at least mischievous. A good example would be 'Heaven Will Protect An Honest Girl' in which a girl's mother advises her on how to avoid being taken to a hotel room for a fate worse than death. Faith reinforced with practical action seems to be the essence of her instruction: 'Breathe a prayer he shall not do it/And then biff him with the cruet/Then Heaven will protect an honest gel!'

The most notable exceptions to the comedy rule were those Music Hall songs that proliferated during World War I and to a lesser extent World War II. These were understandably patriotic. No wartime songs are included here on the basis that they represented an anomaly, a temporary if necessary hijacking of a popular communication channel in the best interests of the nation. The most famous wartime songs were 'Keep The Home Fires Burning', 'Pack Up Your Troubles' and the double-edged recruitment song 'We Don't Want To Lose You (But We Think You Ought To Go)'. In peacetime, though, people did not generally patronise the Music Hall to be reminded of their duty—they went to escape from it and have some fun. Accordingly this is a collection of songs in which fun frequently features. They are often about good nature, resilience and optimism—and this is popular music from a period in Britain's social history that might at times seem to militate strongly against those responses. The golden years of the British Music Hall spanned considerable hardship and privation, not just for its predominantly working-class audience but for some of its performers too. We remember the successes but we tend to forget that not every act was a success. Some performers failed dismally. Some survived on low pay and some became briefly entangled in 'The Music Hall War', a short 1907 industrial dispute between performers and theatre owners stemming from an extra imposed workload. Marie Lloyd could name her price but joined the dispute anyway, saying, 'We are fighting not for ourselves, but for the poorer members of the profession, earning thirty shillings to £3 a week. For this they have to do double turns, and now matinées have been added as well. These poor things have been compelled to submit to unfair terms of employment.' Lloyd was no stranger to unhappiness herself, although her personal demons lay elsewhere. The last time she sang 'I'm One Of The Ruins That Cromwell Knocked About A Bit' the song's central gag about a worse-for-wear woman tottering out of a pub called The Cromwell still raised a laugh from her north London audience, but in real life the singer had been knocked about more than a bit by her last husband and had taken refuge in drink. On the occasion of this 1922 performance in Edmonton, her staggering gait was no piece of comic acting and she collapsed onstage, dying three days later.

She was 52 and had been singing in the halls for 38 of her years. The following songs come with accompanying notes which, where possible, offer some background information or try to explain a few of the references that the passing years may have made more obscure than they were originally. One or two song lyrics seek to render regional accents and while this is a useful reminder that London was far from the only centre for Music Hall, on occasions the phonetic rendering of local pronunciations can be problematic. Such obstacles are few and, generally speaking, this book lets the reader sing or play the very songs that brought entertainment to countless audiences who lived between the mid-19th and 20th centuries and paid their pennies gladly to hear the stars make good-natured fun of life's earthy perils and pleasures. One or two of their heroes and heroines lived long enough to witness the rise of the movies, the advent of television and the widespread availability of cheap gramophone records—some of the very things that helped consign Music Hall to the history books. Today you can find clips of Max Miller appearing at the Metropole in Paddington on YouTube, and of course most of the Music Hall stars left behind recordings of their most popular songs. Yet it was the songs themselves—some sung by various performers, some forever associated with one individual—that told the real story of the Music Hall. Here is a generous selection of them. I should add a note of gratitude to a previous author. Peter Davison's American-published 1971 book about the British Music Hall provided the basis for the present song selection. Although I have omitted some of his song choices and added others, his compilation proved an insightful one. My own song notes presented here have sometimes been influenced by an opinion of his as well as the observations of other commentators. Each generation brings its own cultural perspective to the songs of the past and I have tried here to present something of the enduring vitality and richness of the songs of the Music Hall while trying to contextualise them for the present-day reader.

Graham Vickers, 2013

9

GOING U^P

Songs of Social Aspiration

Wanting to move up the social scale was a theme that recurred in the world of the Music Hall. It was not always seen as a good thing and — as 'Wotcher 'Ria' demonstrates — the would-be social climber was as likely to meet with ridicule from her own class as with resistance from those whose ranks she aspired to join. Meanwhile 'Champagne Charlie' was a stereotypical upper-class lounger, an invented toff whose bubbly-fuelled lifestyle might be envied but whose conspicuous wealth kept him remote from the audience's wildest dreams. In 'If It Wasn't For The 'Ouses In Between' the costermonger's own bucolic fantasy is equally unattainable, but his aspirational bid is as affecting as it is absurd in its doomed attempts to transform shabby urban reality into a pastoral paradise.

CHAMPAGNE CHARLIE
Sung by George Leybourne.

Words and Music by Alfred Lee.

Verse 1

I've seen a deal of gaiety
Throughout my noisy life,
With all my grand accomplishments
I never could get a wife.
The thing I most excel in is
The P.R.F.G. game,
A noise all night, in bed all day,
And swimming in Champagne.

Chorus

For Champagne Charlie is my name,
Champagne Charlie is my game,
Good for any game at night, my boys,
Good for any game at night, my boys.
For Champagne Charlie is my name,
Champagne Charlie is my game,
Good for any game at night, my boys,
Who'll come and join me in a spree?

Verse 2

The way I gained my title's
By a hobby which I've got
Of never letting others pay
However long the shot;
Whoever drinks at my expense
Are treated all the same,
From Dukes and Lords, to cabmen down,
I make them drink Champagne.

Verse 3

From Coffee and from Supper Rooms,
From Poplar to Pall Mall,
The girls, on seeing me, exclaim
"Oh, what a Champagne Swell!"
The notion 'tis of everyone
If 'twere not for my name,
And causing so much to be drunk,
They'd never make Champagne.

Verse 4

Some epicures like Burgundy,
Hock, Claret, and Moselle,
But Moet's vintage only
Satisfies this Champagne swell.
What matter if to bed I go
Dull head and muddled thick,
A bottle in the morning
Sets me right then very quick.

Verse 5

Perhaps you fancy what I say
Is nothing else but chaff,
And only done, like other songs
To merely raise a laugh.
To prove that I am not in jest,
Each man a bottle of Cham.
I'll stand fizz round, yes that I will,
And stand it like a lamb.

In 1944 Ealing Studios tried to recreate the atmosphere of the early Music Hall of the mid-19th century, and the song title they borrowed for their film was 'Champagne Charlie'. It starred Tommy Trinder, a popular comedian of the day, who played Champagne Charlie's real-life singer, George Leybourne. The number had been a successful one in its day and, in the film as in life, it served as Leybourne's main weapon in a professional rivalry which pitted him against Alfred Vance, played by Stanley Holloway. Vance responded with a song called 'Cliquot Cliquot' so starting an alcohol-themed professional duel which probably did neither performer any harm. Leybourne was the leading exponent of an early Music Hall style known as *Lion Comique*, a parodic personification of an upper-class lifestyle of luxury and excess that now seems to sit awkwardly with the defining spirit of classic Music Hall. Soon it would be the affectionately comic exaggeration of working-class concerns that attracted audiences, not the conspicuous display of unimaginable wealth. George Leybourne always played the toff, handsome, expensively if ostentatiously dressed, extolling the virtues of the extravagant night life in London's West End. He and his 'Champagne Charlie' ditty characterised a kind of fantasy existence that well-paid Leybourne himself might enjoy but was hardly within the reach of ordinary mortals such as his audience.

There now seems something mean-spirited about this notion of conspicuous consumption being dangled before the masses and there is little evidence of George Leybourne being a particularly warm man, despite his professional charm and his occasional real-life re-enactment of the final verse's generous gesture: standing the house a round of champagne. It is more than likely that the champagne merchants who had an interest in all the free publicity Leybourne brought them supported him in these well-publicised *largesses*. Certainly he entered into a celebrity deal with Moët & Chandon to endorse their product, which is probably why Alfred Vance aligned himself with rivals Veuve Cliquot. Meanwhile the 'drink duel' prompted yet more alcohol product placements in the music halls, 'Barclay's Beer' being championed by Harry Clifton and the less specific 'Beautiful Beer' by Vance himself.

In retrospect, Trinder seems to have been an odd choice to play the self-styled boulevardier George Leybourne since in his own career he was a rather combative south London comedian whose *shtick* was to puncture social pretension while projecting himself as the salt of the earth. In later life he presented television's belated weekly version of variety, *Sunday Night At The London Palladium* and in hosting its game show slot, *Beat The Clock*, he inadvertently revealed a scathing side to his carefully cultivated image as a common man when called upon to deal with members of the audience.

'Champagne Charlie', first performed at the Sun Music Hall, Knightsbridge in 1867, is a song that retains its melodic appeal despite its brash 'loadsamoney' message. If it pre-dates the spirit of true Music Hall, it was still an early part of that tradition, defining a stereotype that must have had its appeal, however shortlived. Moralists may derive some *schadenfreude* from the fact that George Leybourne, born Joe Sanders in Gateshead and who for a time became the high-living toff he impersonated, eventually saw his career decline and he ended his days in poverty in Islington. He was 42 years old.

IF IT WASN'T FOR
THE 'OUSES IN BETWEEN

Sung by Gus Elen.

Words by Edgar Bateman. Music by George le Brunn.
© Copyright Francis, Day & Hunter, Ltd.
All Rights Reserved. International Copyright Secured.

Moderato

If you saw my lit-tle back-yard, "Wot a pret-ty spot" you'd cry, It's a pic-ture on a sun-ny sum-mer day; Wiv the tur-nip tops and cab-ba-ges wot peo-ples does-n't buy I makes it on a Sun-day look all gay. The neigh-bours finks I grow 'em and you'd fan-cy you're in Kent, Or at Ep-som if you gaze in-to the mews. It's a won-der as the land-lord does-n't want to raise the rent, Be-cause we've got such nob-by dis-tant views.

Chorus

Oh it real-ly is a wer-ry pret-ty gar-den, And Ching-ford to the east-ward could be seen; Wiv a lad-der and some glass-es, You could see to 'Ack-ney Marsh-es, If it was-n' for the 'ous-es in be-tween.

Verse 1

If you saw my little backyard, "Wot a pretty spot!" you'd cry,
It's a picture on a sunny summer day;
Wiv the turnip tops and cabbages wot peoples doesn't buy
I makes it on a Sunday look all gay.
The neighbours finks I grow 'em and you'd fancy you're in Kent,
Or at Epsom if you gaze into the mews.
It's a wonder as the landlord doesn't want to raise the rent.
Because we've got such nobby distant views.

Chorus

Oh it really is a wery pretty garden
And Chingford to the eastward could be seen;
Wiv a ladder and some glasses,
You could see to 'Ackney Marshes,
If it wasn't for the 'ouses in between.

Verse 2

We're as countrified as can be wiv a clothes prop for a tree,
The tub-stool makes a rustic little stile;
Ev'ry time the bloomin' clock strikes there's a cuckoo sings to me,
And I've painted up "To Leather Lane a mile."
Wiv tomatoes and wiv radishes wot 'adn't any sale,
The backyard looks a puffick mass o' bloom;
And I've made a little beehive wiv some beetles in a pail,
And a pitchfork wiv a handle of a broom.

Chorus

Oh it really is a wery pretty garden,
And Rye 'ouse from the cock-loft could be seen:
Where the chickweed man undresses,
To bathe 'mong the watercresses,
If it wasn't for the 'ouses in between.

▶

Verse 3

There's the bunny shares 'is egg box
wiv the cross-eyed cock and hen
Though they 'as got the pip and
him the morf;
In a dog's 'ouse on the line-post there
was pigeons nine or ten,
Till someone took a brick and
knocked it orf.
The dustcart though it seldom comes,
is just like 'arvest 'ome
And we mean to rig a dairy up some'ow;
Put the donkey in the washouse
wiv some imitation 'orns,
For we're teaching 'im to moo
just like a cah.

Chorus

Oh it really is a wery pretty garden,
And 'Endon to the Westward
could be seen;
And by climbing to the chimbley,
You could see a cross to Wembley,
If it wasn't for the 'ouses in between.

Verse 4

Though the gas works isn't wilets,
they improve the rural scene,
For mountains they would
very nicely pass.
There's the mushrooms in the dust-hole
with the cowcumbers so green,
It only wants a bit o' 'ot-'ouse glass.
I wears this milkman's nightshirt,
and I sits outside all day,
Like the ploughboy cove what's
mizzled o'er the Lea;
And when I goes indoors at night
they dunno what I say,
'Cause my language gets as yokel
as can be.

Chorus

Oh it really is a wery pretty garden,
And soap works from the 'ouse tops
could be seen;
If I got a rope and pulley,
I'd enjoy the breeze more fully,
If it wasn't for the 'ouses in between.

Surely Gus Elen's finest moment and probably one of the best Music Hall songs ever written, 'If It Wasn't for the 'Ouses In Between' juxtaposes comedy and pathos to perfection. It really is a wonderful song. There is no false pity and no false pride in Edgar Bateman's lyrics. They even seem perfectly fashioned for Elen's stage persona as the Coster Comedian so that no explanations are necessary when he starts singing about deploying unsold vegetables to create the illusion of a picturesque garden in his backyard. The song sets up a tension between daily life in the East End of London and an ideal garden suburb, and remarkably that tension has the effect of making us laugh. It has something to do with the obsessive earnestness with which Elen's character pursues his bucolic dream. Surely this is an instance of 'making the best of things' getting out of hand, an obsessive optimism that simply refuses to accept reality. And yet acceptance of reality lies at the heart of his efforts to adapt what is to something that could be. Everything has been done to dress up the grubby urban backyard and reinvent it as something countrified—a mock stile, a rustic signpost, a home-made beehive. His dream still resonates today in countless TV gardening programmes where people seek to cram fishponds and fountains, walkways and rustic decking, pergolas and other features more at home on a country estate, into their modest gardens. Simply put, the little backyard in the song is hemmed in by row upon row of houses stretching further than the eye can see. It might not be too fanciful to view this as a visual metaphor for the costermonger's working life which is similarly hemmed in, the countless days stretching ahead like those houses that hide something better beyond. If the sordid backyard can be made to imitate a Kentish garden, then perhaps eventually that procession of working days might also somehow be converted into something more pleasant.

Surmounting all the counterfeit country touches are the panoramic views. They face east, west, north and south, but of course they are non-existent. The various hard-won vantage points the singer earnestly recommends ('Wiv a ladder and some glasses…By climbing on the chimbley…If I got a rope and pulley') would only afford a better view of the obstructive houses that lie in between home sweet home and the seductive greenery known to exist beyond—fresh, green and forever invisible.

Despite the contemporary slang used, the song is most elegantly written: every line carries its intended freight of meaning and at least one of the rhymes demonstrates a brilliant ear—a dialect form of 'chimney' ('chimbley') is satisfyingly paired with Wembley. To those with a knowledge of London's geography it will be clear that you'd need a very tall chimbley indeed to spy Wembley from the East End, but it hardly matters because, once again, the 'ouses in between make it an entirely academic question.

THE HUNTSMAN

Performed by Dan Leno for King Edward VII and Queen Alexandra.

Words by George A. Stevens and Albert Perry.
Music by Fred Eplett.
© Copyright Bowerman & Co.
All Rights Reserved. International Copyright Secured.

Allegretto

I'm not a fire-man or a 'tec, as some folks may sup-pose,_____ Al-though per-haps you'd think so, when you gaze up-on my clothes_____ At pre-sent I'm a hunts-man gay, a hunts-man gay am I,_____ And all the la-dies smile at me, as through the air I fly._____

Chorus

A-way, a-way, a-way, a-way! A-way, a-way, a-way we go. I don't know where we go, but still I know we go a-way.

-way, a - way, a - way, a - way! A - way, a - way, a - way we go, I

don' know where we go, but still I know we go a - way!

Verse

I'm not a fireman or a 'tec, as some folks may suppose,
Although perhaps you'd think so, when you gaze upon my clothes.
At present I'm a huntsman gay, a huntsman gay am I,
And all the ladies smile at me, as through the air I fly.

Patter

Fly! Fly! Fly! Now, when you come to think of it,
what a harmless little creature the fly is.
You see the other day I was invited down to the Duchess
of Piccadilly Circus's county seat to attend the meet.
Now when I say "attend the meet," I don't wish
you to mistake me for a pork butcher. No!
I mean hunting the hares. Now, by hunting the hares,
I don't wish you to mistake me for a hairdresser.
To be explicit, hunting the hares means following the hounds;
and they were a lot of hounds, especially Lord De No Oof,
because just to show that I was used to hunting,
I shouted in his ear, "Tally Ho!" He turned pale and
nearly fainted. He thought I said "Tally-man."
But after all, following the hounds is a splendid life.
The bugles buge, the post-horns horn, and the horses horse.

▶

Now, as soon as I received the invitation, I set about getting a huntsman's costume, and you will observe that I got it. Now I'll let you into a secret. This costume was not made for me at all. It's all over me. This is a proper huntsman's costume, because you have to hunt all through it before you can find me. As I stated before, I took the train by the London, Cheatem and Over [the London Chatham and Dover], and as soon as I arrived at Toad-in-the-Hole there was the barrow waiting for me—I beg pardon, I mean the Baron—and when we arrived at the mansion there was an accident. I found that my luggage was missing. Her ladyship remarked, "Perhaps you have left it at the station." I said, "No! no! I don't think so—*very deep in thought*—no, I could not have left it at the station. Ah! I have it." Then I suddenly recollected that I had placed it in my hat for safety—a piece of Sunlight soap, and a packet of Tibbles.

Then the Baron said, "Now we will go to the meet." I couldn't see any meat. I looked round, but only saw a lot of empty plates; I think they must have eaten all the meat for breakfast. Well, then they put me up in a beautiful set of apartments—lovely furniture-ancient; I knew it was ancient when I looked at it. ▶

Dan Leno often dressed in exaggerated costumes to match the characters he impersonated in his comic songs and patter.

Why, the sofa was hard up for a leg. And the bed.
Ah! the bed! Splendid! It was one of those double,
triple, springy, slip-away, stop-wherever-you-are,
no kind of bed at all. You know, sort of a cross-breed,
between a bed and a switchback railway. I never
did see such a lovely bit of architecture in my life.
It was—well, I did not stop to criticise everything in
the room. My mind was so full of hunting. I was
dreaming of hunting all night.

Next morning we came down to breakfast as
happy as hares. And what a fine breakfast we had.
So many different courses—kippers and marmalade.
We thoroughly enjoyed ourselves. Young Lady Evelyn,
the daughter—jolly young cat—flirting with me all
the time. She was squeezing my hand and so on, and
she kept on (just for fun) sticking bits of marmalade
on my face. When we finished, we donned our
costumes and started off to the meet—to the meet.
The horn sounded and pip, pip, away we went on
our bicycles — I mean our chestnuts. When I say
chestnuts, I don't mean stale jokes. No. Horses, horse,
not elephants, horses. Away we dashed over the
dillies and dallies, and I caught the hare. But I could
never see the use of spending all this time and taking
all this trouble in catching the hare. I have come to
the conclusion that it is much easier to go into a poultry
shop and buy one. At any rate, I caught it. I was riding
along, breakneck pace, when I saw something darting
past the hedge. Said I, "That's the hare," and taking
deliberate aim, I exerted my strength and threw my
gun at it. Then I shouted to my friends behind,
"Tally Ho! Tally Ho! Tally Ho! I've got it." Then springing
from my horse, I rushed towards the jungle—I beg
pardon, I mean the hedge — and withdrew the animal.
Then we gazed upon it. And the poor cat was dead. ▶

Chorus

Away, away, away, away, away, away, away we go:
I don't know where we go, but still I know we go away.
Away, away, away, away, away, away, away we go:
I don't know where we go, but still I know we go away.
I've played at various hunting games since I've been on this earth,
But of that class of hunting I never knew the worth.
I won't infer that I have never hunted hares before,
Because at home, when we've had soup, I've found them by the score.

Patter

Well, I had never done any real hunting before. I am
a tripe-dresser by persuasion. So the Baron told me when I
came to the ditch to take it—I took it. Well, when I say
took it, I suppose I took a pint and a half. I would not take
another liqueur of ditch for anything. There was a kind of
blancmange at the bottom, and a verdigiis at the top. Then the
Baron told me to follow the scent. I said, "You follow it, I
have quite enough here to last me for a month!" But although
I don't know much of hunting in the true sense of the word,
I did very well for a beginner. First over the hedge every time—
very often before the horse. You know, the horse is a very
beautiful creature—so affectionate, so docile, so tame, I
love it. Well, I am particularly in love with the horse I rode.
I had not ridden a hundred yards when my affection so overcame
me that I clasped my arms tightly round his neck and would not let go.

Gone away! What do they say that for? There is no
necessity. We know the hares have gone away. In fact, to my idea
they would be very silly to linger about on such occasions.
It stands to reason. Do you mean to tell me that if you were
a hare that you would be waiting about for me to come up with
a gun, loaded with old nails, bits of paper, and scraps of
boot-leather? No! You would have an important appointment
somewhere else. Why, I'd sooner have one little game of hunt
the slipper than forty hunt the hares.

Chorus

'The Huntsman' gives us the famous Dan Leno at his verbose best. Not so much a song as a spoken comic short story with the odd chorus interpolated, this piece was performed by Leno for King Edward VII and Queen Alexandra and it would seem to make considerable demands on the performer's memory and stamina.

Certainly Leno, the idol of the Music Hall, was sick several times on the train journey to Sandringham so worried was he about the ordeal of performing it for royalty. Leno was born George Wild Galvin in Somers Town, London, the son of Music Hall entertainers who had appeared on stage as Mr & Mrs Johnny Wild. Although he performed for less than 20 years, Leno became a Music Hall legend before his death at the age of 44 in 1904. One of the many people much moved by his loss was the contemporary essayist and caricaturist Max Beerbohm, who attempted to evaluate Leno's genius. Unlike Albert Chevalier, wrote Beerbohm, 'Leno was no inaugurator; at most 'he shifted the centre of gravity from song to patter'. His theme was always 'the sordidness of the lower middle class, seen from within. Yet, in his hand, how gloriously it blazed, illuminating and warming! All that trite and unlovely material, how new and beautiful it became for us through Dan Leno's genius!' It was, Beerbohm continued, Leno's personality that made his act what it was universally claimed to be, for he was 'a creature apart, radiating an ethereal essence all his own'. This evaluation sounds a little inflated by the emotion of the moment since Leno, by his own admission, had started out by looking down on Music Hall. A man of some education, Leno had replaced George Bernard Shaw as *The Saturday Review*'s theatre critic in which capacity he wrote the following jaundiced words: 'The mass of people, when it seeks pleasure, does not want to be elevated: it wants to laugh at something beneath its own level. Just as I used to go to Music Halls that I might feel my superiority to the audience, so does the audience go that it might compare itself favourably with the debased rapscallions of the songs.' As already noted, 'The Huntsman' is more a complete act than a song, the sung part being little more than a mock hunting cry. The patter is a relentless parade of puns, malapropisms, absurd situations, wordplay and unexpected associations of ideas.

It all hinges on the inappropriateness of an incompetent working man trying to look at home with the gentry. It was the kind of vibrant scene-painting in words at which Leno excelled. Even in his autobiography, ghost-written but presumably much informed by its claimed author, Leno maintains he 'came into the world a mere child' but became a farthing millionaire with 'an acre and two pints of some of the best wasp-stalking in the kingdom'.

Without his personality to interpret them, Leno's songs and acts, even more than those of other artists, look like less than what he probably made them. As he died in 1904, his recordings were made when techniques were very crude, so although it is possible to hear his voice and gauge something of his approach, such recordings cannot do him justice.

In his tribute, Max Beerbohm also foresaw the talking movie. 'Some day, no doubt, the phonograph and the bioscope will have been so adjusted to each other that we shall see and hear past actors and singers as well as though they were alive before us' he guessed, with some accuracy back in 1904, 23 years before the event. 'I wish Dan Leno could have been thus immortalised. No actor of our times deserved immortality as well as he.'

Right: Dan Leno, idol of the Music Hall, making an uncharacteristic appearance as himself.

WOTCHER 'RIA
Sung by Bessie Bellwood and Nelly Farren.

Words by Will Herbert and Music by Bessie Bellwood. Arranged by George Ison.

Allegretto

I am a girl what's-a-do-ing we-ry well in the we-ge-ta-ble line, And as I'd sav'd a bob or two, I thought I'd cut a shine. So I goes and buys some tog-ger-y, These 'ere we-ry clothes you see, And with the mon-ey I had left I thought I'd have a spree. So I goes in-to a mus-ic hall where I'd oft-en been a-fore, I don't go in the gal-ler-y but on the bot-tom floor; I sits down by the Chair-man and calls for a pot of Stout, My pals in the gal-ler-y spot-ted me, and they all com-menced to shout:

Chorus

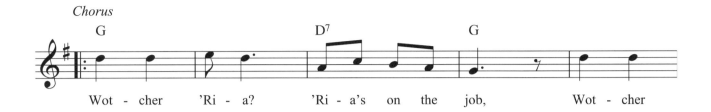

Wot - cher 'Ri - a? 'Ri - a's on the job, Wot - cher

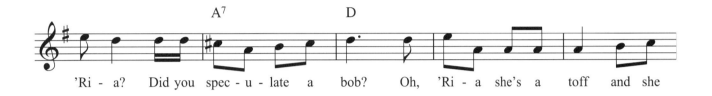

'Ri - a? Did you spec - u - late a bob? Oh, 'Ri - a she's a toff and she

looks im - men - si - koff, And they all shout-ed Wot - cher 'Ri - a?

Verse 1

I am a girl what's doing wery well in the wegetable line,
And as I'd saved a bob or two, I thought I'd cut a shine.
So I goes and buys some toggery, these 'ere wery clothes you see,
And with the money I had left I thought I'd have a spree.
So I goes into a music hall where I'd often been afore,
I don't go in the gallery but on the bottom floor;
I sits down by the Chairman and calls for a pot of Stout,
My pals in the gallery spotted me and they all commenced to shout:

Chorus

Wotcher 'Ria? 'Ria's on the job
Wotcher 'Ria? Did you speculate a bob?
Oh, 'Ria she's a toff
And she looks immensikoff,
And they all shouted, Wotcher 'Ria? ▶

Verse 2

Of course I chaffed them back again, but it worn't a bit of use.
The poor old Chairman's baldie head they treated with abuse;
They threw an orange down at me, it went bang inside a pot,
The beer went up like a fountain, and a toff copped all the lot;
It went slap in his chevy, and it made an awful mess,
But what gave me the needle was, it spoilt me blooming dress.
I thought it was getting rather warm, so I goes towards the door,
When a man shoves out his gammy leg, and I fell smack on the floor.

Spoken

I turned round and spoke to him wery politely. I said,
"What cher want to go and shove your jolly old gammy leg out like
that for?" He said, "I beg your pardon, Madam." I says, "Beg
nothing, you jolly old josserl" He says. "Don't you be saucy
or I shall get you chucked out." When my pals spot I'm having
a row, and they see the old man has got a wooden leg, they shout
out, "Wotcher! Half a man and half a tree?!"

Chorus

Verse 3

Now the gent that keeps the Music Hall he patters to the bloke,
Of course they blamed it all on me, but I couldn't see the joke.
So I upped and told the governor as how he'd shoved me down,
And with his jolly old wooden leg, tore the frilling off my gown.
But law bless you! It worn't a bit of use, the toff was on the job.
They said, "Outside!" and out I went, and they stuck to my bob.
Of course I left so wild, to think how I'd been taken down,
Next time I'll go in the gallery with my pals, you bet a crown.

Spoken

You don't catch me going chucking my money away, trying
to be a toff any more—the way they served me wasn't so very
polite. They brought the chucker-out and he said, "Come on,
'Ria, you've been kicking up a pretty row," he says, "Come
on, outside." I says, "Shan't, shan't! There you are!
Shan't!!" He took hold of me and handed me out, just as
though I'd been a sack of taters. When I got outside, my
young man was waiting. So he says, "Serves you jolly well
right, 'Ria! You shouldn't try to be a lady, 'cause it
don't suit yer." Just then my pals were coming out of the
gallery and they all commenced shouting:

Chorus

Bessie Bellwood was one of the first of the great women characters of Music Hall, perhaps because she so well personified the spirit of the genre in its rumbustious heyday. She could work the liveliest saloon crowd in the days when a chairman tried to instil order into the often lively proceedings, and was known for being generous with both her money and her time, volunteering personally to minister to the needy, the sick and the dying.

'Wotcher 'Ria' (or 'What Cheer 'Ria' to give it its quaint contemporary spelling) was Bellwood's best-known song, and its lyric casts her as a vegetable seller who has dressed up to the nines to go to the Music Hall. There she is teased by a group of acquaintances up in the gallery who believe she is putting on airs down on the main floor among the well-to-do patrons. 'Ria then becomes involved in a slapstick commotion leading to her being thrown out in disarray. This self-deprecating song amused contemporary audiences who recognised Bessie Bellwood to be a forthright and unpretentious woman who, in her former East End life as Kathleen Mahoney, had been no more socially elevated than 'Ria (a chirpy contraction of 'Maria' that underscores her modest social standing). The song's theme of fitting in

socially, or not, is further underlined by the contrast between her essentially good-natured chaffing friends in the gallery and the toffs (whose numbers she has infiltrated in her aspirational outfit) down below with whom she clashes when trying to beat a hasty retreat. The blame for the minor affray is put squarely onto 'Ria, and so she is ejected with a torn and beer-stained dress—but no refund. The moral of the song might be Henry David Thoreau's aphorism 'Beware of all ventures that require new clothes' because it was 'Ria's prideful wish to demonstrate that she was doing well in trade by dressing up and then showing off that led to her embarrassment. In fairness it is worth remembering that her squabble with the toffs was initiated not by them but by her friends mocking her harmless bit of social climbing. Even her 'young man' seems short on sympathy, greeting her by saying 'Serves you jolly well right…you shouldn't try to be a lady "cause it don't suit yer". In this way the main obstacle to 'Ria's bit of social pretension seems not to be the class she playfully pretends to aspire to, but the class to which she already belongs. Like many Music Hall songs, 'Wotcher 'Ria' has patter between the verses which extends the song and provides a change of pace that allows for several reiterations of the bracing chorus.

LET

DOWN

Songs of Disappointment

Songs of parting, missed opportunities, loss and desertion also abound in the Music Hall repertoire. We should not necessarily assume that there was more disenchantment about in the golden years of the halls, just less media through which to bemoan it. 'Waiting At The Church' and 'Are We To Part Like This, Bill?' are pretty transparent stories of love affairs doomed, but 'My Old Man (Said Follow The Van)', not always thought of as a tale of loss, does leave itself open to interpretation as being not just an amusing song about a couple abandoning their premises but more ominously one of a husband seizing the opportunity to ditch his wife into the bargain.

ARE WE TO PART LIKE THIS, BILL?

Sung by Kate Carney.

Words and Music by Harry Castling and Charles Collins.
© Copyright: B. Feldman & Co., Ltd.
All Rights Reserved. International Copyright Secured.

Andante

Three weeks a - go, no lon - ger, I was as gay as a bird on the wing, But since me and Bill have been part - ed, you know, Life is a blank and it's changed ev - 'ry - thing. I saw him out with an - oth - er that night, None can guess how___ I felt at the sight, With___ tears in my eyes that I tried to keep back, I crept to his side and said:_____

Verse 1

Three weeks ago, no longer,
I was as gay as a bird on the wing,
But since me and Bill have been parted, you know,
Life is a blank and it's changed ev'rything.
I saw him out with another that night,
None can guess how I felt at the sight,
With tears in my eyes that I tried to keep back,
I crept to his side and said:

Chorus

Are we to part like this, Bill,
Are we to part this way?
Who's it to be, 'er or me?
Don't be a-frightened to say.
If everything's over between us,
Don't never pass me by,
'Cos you and me still friends can be,
For the sake of the days gone by.
We went to school together,
Lived side by side, me and Bill, in the Mews.
When 'e was ill, too, I stayed up for nights,
Nursed him—to do it I'd never refuse;
'E used to tell me his wife I should be—
I never thought that he'd turn against me,
Sleeping or waking, at work or at home,
I find myself murmuring this:

Verse 2

Down in a little laundry,
Me and 'er work side by side every day;
She was my pal and I looked to 'er well,
Trusted and helped 'er in every way.
Still if my Bill cares for 'er more than me,
I wish 'em no harm—no, but prosperity;
I try to forget him, but each day I find
These words running through my mind:

Chorus

Kate Carney.

For today's tastes the Music Hall may seem to have had more than its fair share of sentimentality. From time to time, though, the hard facts of a very ordinary life were conveyed in such a way that could be genuinely affecting rather than maudlin or mawkish. Kate Carney's 'Are We To Part Like This, Bill?' is a case in point and, despite some awkwardness in the language, it does manage to make its pathos convincing and acceptable, not least because of Charles Collins' very pretty melody. The lyrics, by Harry Castling, are a curious mixture of the banal ('Life is a blank, and it's changed everything') and expressions of selflessness pitched somewhere between altruism and self-martyrdom. Even so, the overall effect is one of personal heartbreak born of a real-life painful experience rather than some ironic story concocted by a professional lyricist adept at working an audience's emotions.

Kate Carney, sometimes known as the Coster Comedienne, made her name with Irish songs despite being born in Streatham, south London. Eventually she was identified as a cockney performer, albeit one whose strong, melodic voice and faultless diction betrayed nothing of either the Emerald Isle or the East End. In this song she manages to suggest the same sort of affinity with the way of life she describes as Bessie Bellwood does in 'Wotcher 'Ria'. 'Are We To Part Like This, Bill?' vividly evokes living in a place whose smallness suddenly becomes a curse because Bill and his former girl cannot help but meet, nor can she help but see him out with the new girl. The two girls even work side by side, here turning the kind of close-knit community often praised for its merits into a confined neighbourhood prison where the present and the past (the couple even went to school together) conspire to add to the singer's pain. There is no obvious escape. Worse still, despite previous assurances from Bill that he wanted to marry her, it seems that the arrival of the new girlfriend reveals his former affection to have been rather more shallow than had been assumed. 'Are We To Part Like This, Bill?' therefore comes over as a more thoughtful and deeply felt little musical drama than so many more dramatic Music Hall tales of passion lost and hearts broken.

BANG WENT THE
CHANCE OF A LIFETIME Sung by George Robey.

Words and Music by Sax Rohmer.
© Copyright: 1908, Francis, Day & Hunter, Ltd.
All Rights Reserved. International Copyright Secured.

Now old aunt Re-bec-ca is rich;___ She's the Dow-a-ger Duch-ess of Did-dle___ when she dies I in-her-it a mil-lion or so, But the old girl's as fit as a fid-dle,___ Whilst gun-ning the moors on the twelfth,___ in a quiet lone-ly spot by the sea,___ I saw some-one there by the cliff. I de-clare,'Twas the Dow-a-ger Duch-ess of D!

Chorus

At that crit-i-cal mo-ment some birds came in sight, So I uppped with my gun and I blazed left and right; And I near-ly hit aunt-ie! Yes near-ly, not *quite!* And *bang* went the chance of a life-time!

Verse 1

Now old aunt Rebecca is rich;
She's the Dowager Duchess of Diddle.
When she dies I inherit a million or so,
But the old girl's as fit as a fiddle.
Whilst gunning the moors on the twelfth,
In a quiet lonely spot by the sea,
I saw someone there by the cliff, I declare,
'Twas the Dowager Duchess of D!

Chorus

At that critical moment some birds came in sight,
So I upped with my gun and I blazed left and right;
And I nearly hit auntie! Yes—nearly, not quite!
And bang went the chance of a lifetime.

Patter

'Twas a pity, I say, 'twas a pity, I might have
struck her with one of the pellets—however:

Verse 2

Returning one night from a ball,
In a mellowish mood and reflective,
I saw a strange light in a bank—I said, "Ha!"
(Spoken)
Like that, "Ha!" (*exaggerated surprise*)
I'll play Sherlock Holmes the detective.
(Sung)
A half-open window I spied,
And inside I proceeded to slip;
There a burglar I saw forcing wide the safe door,
So I held him in muscular grip!

Chorus

But he slipped and he bunked, he was wiry and thin;
And the safe was wide open and slap full of "tin"!
I drew a deep breath—then two coppers rushed in! And
bang went the chance of a lifetime. ▶

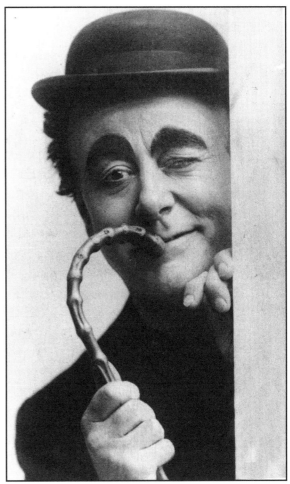

*George Robey in his most familiar stage guise with exaggerated
eyebrows, distinctive hat and walking cane.*

Patter
’Twas a pity, I say, ’twas a pity.
I might have got some of the, er, however,
Oh, I hardly like to tell you the,
er, personal, however—

Verse 3
Now the wife and her mother
(*Spoken:* Oh, the mother!), last June,
Went to stay with the Marquis de Caxey,
(*Spoken:* She’s alright, too—)
So I saw them safe off in a taxi.
At somewhere about ten o’clock
Came a telegram—Heavens alive!—
Poor dear Ma and the wife! Fearful smash! Loss of life!
Total wreck of the eight-forty-five!

Chorus
’Twas a terrible crash, eighty passengers slain!
And I manfully struggled my tears to restrain,
When the ghastly news reached me—
they’d both missed the train!
And bang went the chance of a lifetime! (*Sobs*)

Verse 4
Once I courted a sweet winsome wench
(*Amorous sighs*)
She was nineteen and also an heiress,
It’s nice when a girl is a Venus galore
And also a millionairess!
I wooed her, I wooed, I won (*Spoken:* Wow, wow)
“My darling,” she said, “I am thine!” (*Sighs*)
She swore she'd be true (*Spoken:* Get away!)
So I thought I would too;
What do you think? I thought it was fine!

Chorus
My sweet Hyacinth, fairest of flowers that blow!
(With a millionaire Pa in Chicago, what ho!)
So I put up the banns, then the wife got to know,
And bang went the chance of a lifetime.

This George Robey song was used by the singer to make the kind of twin appeal to the audience that frequently flourished in the Music Hall: song and patter. The song itself has its own appeal, but the singer's spoken interjections add a conspiratorial element to the performance—a kind of extra-mural commentary that might not be marked by great wit but usually amplified the appeal of hearing him perform the song. The device also plays on the theatrical paradox of suspending disbelief by constantly reminding the audience of the artificiality of the performance while simultaneously asking them to believe in it. 'Bang Went the Chance of a Lifetime' lends itself well to this kind of narrative interplay with its combination of the comic and the macabre as the hapless singer misses out on several fortuitous opportunities that very nearly come off. The first verse is about the failure of a would-be shooting accident that might have resulted in an inheritance. The second concerns foiling a bank robbery and narrowly missing getting away with the loot that was left behind. The third rather dark verse tells of the singer's raised spirits when his wife and mother-in-law are assumed to be on a train that crashes with great loss of life; however, it turns out they have missed the train. The final verse about thwarted bigamy descends into farce since this time it is not fickle fate that scuppers the chance of a lifetime, but the singer's pre-existing marriage of which he could hardly have been unaware. The author of this litany of disappointment (both words and music) was one Arthur Ward, a working-class lad from Birmingham who was not only George Robey's writer and the ghost author of the autobiography of another Music Hall star (Harry Relph, a.k.a. Little Tich), but would go on to become the crime novelist Sax Rohmer under which name he wrote numerous books featuring his famous creation Fu Manchu. Sax Rohmer's final legacy—apart from perhaps setting back the cause of the Chinese immigrant by several decades—was to have his made-up surname appropriated by French film director Maurice Schérer who paired it with Erich von Stroheim's first name to become Éric Rohmer.

George Robey, Britain's self-appointed Prime Minister of Mirth, went on to a distinguished acting career as well as becoming identified with many other Music Hall songs.

"JEERUSALEM'S" DEAD! Sung by Albert Chevalier.

Words by Brian Daly. Music by John Cook.

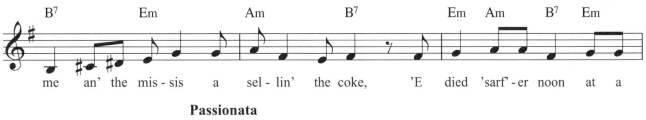

me an' the mis-sis a sel-lin' the coke, 'E died 'sarf'-er noon at a

Passionata

quar - ter ter four, But I think that it's rough-er on me than the moke.

Verse 1

I've 'ad four 'arf-pints at the Magpie an' Stump,
An' two goes o' rum jes ter keep up my sperrits;
My mince-pies are waterin' jes like a pump,
An' they're red as a ferrit's.
'Cos why? 'Tain't the missis nor kids wot I've lost,
But one wot I careful-lie doctored an' fed;
The nussin' an' watchin' 'as turned out a frost,
The Jeerusalem's dead!

Chorus

Yer won't see 'im pullin' the barrer no more,
Wi' me an' the missis a-sellin' the coke.
'E died 's arf'ernoon at a quarter ter four,
But I think that it's rougher on me
than the moke.

Verse 2

'E 'ad a big 'eart and a strong pair o' 'eels,
A temper as short as was e'er manifactured;
In 'arness 'e used ter do 'ornpipes an' reels,
An' my ribs 'e once fractured!
'E bit like the devil, and eat like a 'orse,
An' orfen 'e'd try ter stan' up on 'is 'ead;
It's all over now wiv 'is tricks an' 'is sauce,
The Jeerusalem's dead!

Verse 3

I stroked 'is old 'ead as—'e laid in the stall,
An' some'ow or other I felt I must kiss 'im!
I've a wife an' some youngsters 'e wasn't
Quite all, But I know I shall miss 'im.
There's one thing I'm certain, 'is grub was the best,
An' I've gone short myself ter purvide 'im a bed;
Come 'an 'ave 'arf a pint-there's a lump in my chest
The Jeerusalem's dead!

Albert Chevalier.

As an introduction to one of the great Music Hall stars '"Jeerusalem's" Dead!' tells only part of the story of the man who, scarcely believably, was christened Albert Onesime Britannicus Gwathveoyd Louis Chevalier when he was born in London's Notting Hill in 1861. At the age of 14, Albert temporarily pruned this bizarre name, Anglicising Chevalier to Knight to perform as Albert Knight in amateur dramatics. A professional career as an actor followed but only at the age of 30, and after a long spell of unemployment, did Albert (with 'Chevalier' now restored) become a Music Hall performer. He invented the persona of a costermonger and even built a self-contained touring entertainment around his act. It was the most unlikely of career changes since this quiet and thoughtful man had little in common with the Music Hall ethos. No one was more surprised than he was when he became a huge success.

'"Jeerusalem's" Dead!' and the other Chevalier song in this collection 'The Future Mrs 'Awkins', both represent something at which he excelled: the emotional song that was not weighed down with sentimentality. In addition to such songs (which should also include his famously emotive 'My Old Dutch', a paean to a faithful wife of 40 years), Chevalier performed parodies, a pseudo-French song, dialect numbers and even a toff song 'The Johnnie's Serenade', perhaps a nod to the career of his father in law, George Leybourne, one of Music Hall's leading *Lions Comique* and the performer of 'Champagne Charlie'.

'"Jeerusalem's" Dead!' finds Chevalier in his tradesman guise, lamenting the death of a donkey who was not a pet in the modern sense but a working animal that was in effect a vital piece of industrial equipment in the tradesman's coke delivery trade. (In case any young readers unfamiliar with traditional fossil fuels should get the wrong idea, this coke was neither a soft drink nor a narcotic but a lightweight derivative of coal that produced very little smoke when burned in stoves or grates). The Jeerusalem (a nickname for a donkey derived from the biblical episode of Christ's Palm Sunday entry into Jerusalem on such a beast) is mourned by his owner with a mixture of commercial alarm and genuine grief. Tearfully tipsy he recalls how he looked after the creature which, along with its dependable strength, could also

display a combative and spirited temperament, and how he would go without food himself so that the animal should be fed. The song could have turned out to be unbearably sentimental yet somehow it presents its blend of affection and pragmatism in an unaffected way. In doing so it encapsulates another less obvious aspect of Music Hall. As well as the bawdy comic song, the sentimental ballad and the well-observed social commentary, a good Music Hall song could also sometimes tap into a vein of seriousness that was neither solemn nor sermonising but simply affecting.

MY OLD MAN
(SAID FOLLOW THE VAN) Sung by Marie Lloyd.

Words and Music by Fred W. Leigh and Charles Collins.

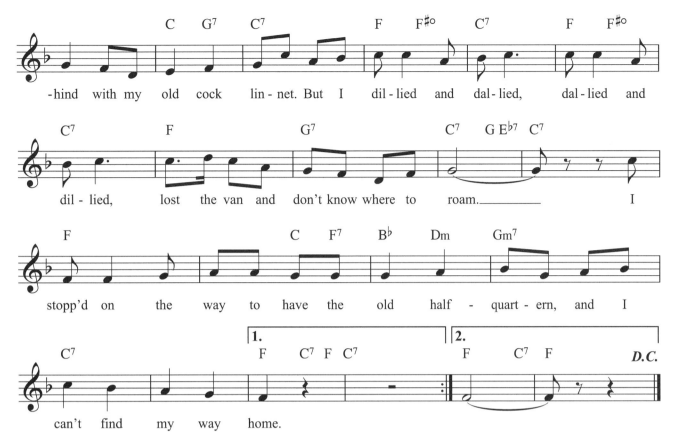

Verse 1

We had to move away,
'cos the rent we couldn't pay,
The moving van came round just after dark:
There was me and my old man,
shoving things inside the van,
Which we'd often done before, let me remark.
We packed all that could be packed in the van,
and that's a fact:
And we got inside all we could get inside,
Then we packed all we could pack
on the tailboard at the back,
'Till there wasn't any room for me inside.

Chorus 1

My old man said, "Follow the van,
don't dilly dally on the way!"
Off went the cart with the home packed in it,
I walked behind with my old cock linnet.
But I dillied and dallied, dallied and dillied,
Lost the van and don't know where to roam.
I stopp'd on the way to have the old half quartern,
And I can't find my way home.

Verse 2

I gave a helping hand with the marble
wash-hand-stand,
And straight, we wasn't getting on so bad.
All at once the carman bloke had an accident
and broke
Well, the nicest bit of china that we had.
You'll understand of course,
I was cross about the loss,
Same as any other human woman would.
But I soon got over that, what with "two-out"
and a chat
'Cos it's little things like that what does you good.

Chorus 2

My old man said, "Follow the van,
don't dilly dally on the way!"
Off went the cart with the home packed in it,
I walked behind with my old cock linnet.
But I dillied and dallied, dallied and dillied,
Lost the van and don't know where to roam.
You can't trust the "specials" like the old time
"coppers"
When you can't find your way home.

One of the greatest of all Music Hall songs fell to Marie Lloyd to sing although, unlike some of her other material, this one would surely have been a success whoever sang it. 'My Old Man (Said Follow The Van)' is a brilliant vignette of 'a moonlight flit' in which a working-class couple, having failed to pay the rent, have to move home surreptitiously after dark with all of their belongings. The beginning of that scene-setting verse is a masterpiece of assured and colourful writing: We had to move away, 'cos the rent we couldn't pay/The moving van came round just after dark/There was me and my old man shoving things inside the van/As we'd often done before, might I remark.

It paints a picture of a commonplace occurrence among the working class of the day (and no doubt among other classes too with larger sums involved) but here the already disruptive experience is made worse by lack of space in the van which means that the wife has to follow on foot clutching a birdcage containing a pet linnet. Instructed not to 'dilly-dally' (dawdle) she does just that, loses her way and so becomes separated from van, home and husband. The plaintive last line

'When you can't find your way 'ome' takes on extra resonance since 'home' is now a quite unfamiliar destination. The song has acquired several different last lines in which various explanations are offered for her getting lost and left behind (although logic suggests that it was always unlikely that she could keep pace with a motor vehicle, even if she were unburdened by her old cock linnet):

• Unreliable directions from a special constable who, not being a regular, is less familiar with his beat ('You can't trust a special like an old time copper').

• An ill-advised break for refreshment ('I stopped on the way to have me old half quarten' or 'I had to stop to have a drop of tiddly in the pub').

• The dawning realisation that, as the alternative chorus states, 'you can't trust a man when your life's in a van'.

The song, written by Fred W. Leigh and Charles Collins, long outlived Music Hall to resurface in countless TV shows over the years from *The Sweeney* to *The Muppet Show*. It was even sung in J. Lee Thompson's well-regarded 1958 war film *Ice-Cold In Alex*, a movie not otherwise noted for its musical content. Often performed as the most recognisable Music

Hall song for a general audience, it has therefore become iconic, instantly conjuring an image of 'traditional Britishness' where atmosphere is more important than accuracy. In this spirit, comedian Jerry Seinfeld joined in a stagey pub singalong of 'My Old Man' in one of his American Express TV commercials. Even if the song was good enough to succeed without Marie Lloyd, she was its ideal interpreter. Despite her huge fame and considerable wealth, she was a warm, down-to-earth woman in whom a combination of sex appeal and poor judgement had resulted in a series of not altogether successful marriages. She brought just the right blend of cockney pluck and vulnerability to 'My Old Man'. The song, like her life, is sadder at heart than it sounds on the surface.

Marie Lloyd, a working-class heroine from Hoxton in London, dolled up as a well-to-do woman— which is what she became as one of Music Hall's highest-paid stars.

NANNY Sung by Harry Lauder.

Words and Music by Harry Lauder and J. H. Milligan.
© Copyright: 1915, Francis, Day & Hunter, Ltd.
All Rights Reserved. International Copyright Secured.

I've just come here the nicht to ask you for your sym-pa-thy, The on-ly lass I ev-er had frae me has gone a-way. It hap-pened o'er a quar-rel that we had last Sun-day nicht, She said I was in the wrong but I said I was right. My heart is near-ly bro-ken, at times I think I'll choke When I think a-bout the prom-is-es she made. She told me once sin-cere-ly that she loved me, Oh! So dear-ly, So I've writ-ten her a let-ter and I've said:

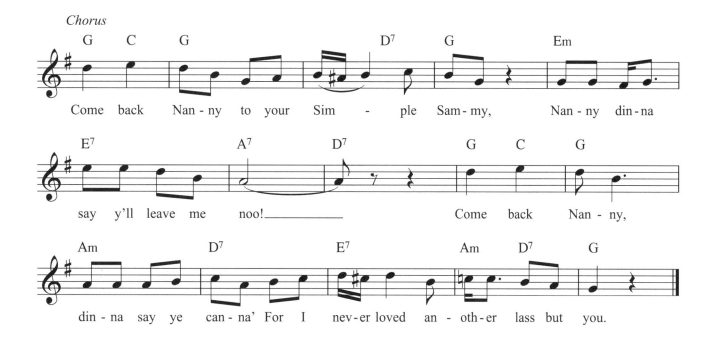

Chorus

Come back Nanny to your Simple Sammy, Nanny dinna say y'll leave me noo! Come back Nanny, dinna say ye canna' For I never loved another lass but you.

Verse 1

I've just come here the nicht to ask you for your sympathy,
The only lass I ever had frae me has gone away.
It happened o'er a quarrel that we had last Sunday nicht,
She said I was in the wrong but I said I was right.
My heart is nearly broken; at times I think I'll choke
When I think about the promises she made. (*Mock anguish*)
She told me once sincerely, that she loved me, Oh! So dearly,
So I've written her a letter and I've said:

Chorus

Come back Nanny to your simple Sammy,
Nanny dinna say y'll leave me noo!
Come back Nanny, dinna say ye canna'
For I never loved another lass but you. ▶

Verse 2

I really don't know what to do, I've such a burning pain,
Burning like a poultice in below my watch and chain.
I really did look forward to lead such a happy life,
But that can never be, unless she says she'll be my wife.
We used to go for long walks nearly every other night,
We used to wander doon the lover's lane
Yon was such a time of bliss, I did nothing else but kiss her,
I'll never kiss another lass again.

Patter

I'll do something desperate. I'll disfigure myself for life.
I know what I'll do, grow a whisker and cut my hair!
If I were to blame, I'd give in; but I'm not to blame. I know
who's to blame. I know. It's her mother. She's the one.
Mind you, a nice enough woman to look at. Oh! Quite nice.
But you've got to look at her quick then run for your life.
Y'see Nanny's mother has a big family. She's got six children
and three boys and it was this wee boy's birthday. That
was the whole cause of it, y'see, because Nanny's mother
told Nanny to write me and invite me to come down to
the party. That is to the birthday party. Y'see, because
there was bacon and dumplings, and oh! I can eat dumplings,
I can eat dumplings with anybody. So that was the whole
cause of it. I never, I never, I never got a currant out of
that dumpling. Oh, dear me! When I think about it ye know—
Oh! It's her mother, that's the one that's to blame for it all.
Because Nanny knows that I love her. Oh! She knows that
I love her alright, and her mother knows that I love her.
I'm the first sweetheart Nanny ever had, and I believe
she's only doing this quarreling to try my sincerity.
And I believe she is here the nicht, listening if I'm saying
anything about her. (**Business: Looks round the audience,
says he sees her, and sings to her:**)

Chorus

Harry Lauder, born Henry Lauder in 1870 in Edinburgh, started his working life in the mills of Scotland, became a miner in Hamilton and soon began playing the local halls of Lanarkshire. It took him time to build his act and he was 35 by the time he finally triumphed at the Theatre Royal, Glasgow in a pantomime for which he wrote and sang 'I Love A Lassie'. The song made him a star in Britain and he went on to tour the world for 40 years usually kitted out in full Scottish regalia: kilt with sporran, Tam O'Shanter and curly walking stick. Many of his best-known songs are sentimental although he did have some of the comic-pathetic variety.

'Nanny' would seem to be one of these, at least in intent, but it is a curious offering from the man Winston Churchill called 'Scotland's greatest ever ambassador'. It tells of a lovers' quarrel, yet the tune of the chorus is cheerful to the point of being exultant. Furthermore, when singing it Lauder would often deliberately overplay the tearfulness for comic effect. The cause of the quarrel is not adequately explained, nor is this omission acknowledged, with the result that the tone of the song is confused. The version included here is a hybrid of two recorded performances, a long one that more or less conforms to the original printed version, and a shorter one. The patter seems to have undergone several changes each time Lauder performed it, perhaps because, being neither particularly comic nor particularly strong on pathos, it was something he was always seeking to improve. Some Music Hall songs pull off the trick of making successful transitions between comedy and pathos but 'Nanny' always seemed to be a work in progress that never quite came together. Lauder probably lost no sleep over it. He became a well-paid, much-admired Scottish performer the world over making 22 tours of the US and also visiting Australia frequently. In later years, the notion of Scottishness being signified by a traditional costume and songs like 'Roamin' In The Gloamin" fell out of fashion, but Harry Lauder was the first to make it work and it sustained him for a long lifetime. Outliving both his wife and his son (who was killed in action in December 1916 in France), Sir Harry Lauder died aged 79 in Strathaven, Lanarkshire, in 1950.

WAITING AT THE CHURCH

Sung by Harry Lauder.

Words by Fred W. Leigh. Music by Henry E. Pether.

Allegro moderato

I'm in a nice bit of trou-ble, I con-fess Some-bo-dy with me has had a game. I should by now be a proud and hap-py bride, But I've still got to keep my sin-gle name. I was pro-posed to by O-ba-di-ah Binks In a ve-ry gen-tle man-ly way; Lent him all my mon-ey so that he could buy a home, And punc-tual-ly at twelve o'clock to-day

Chorus

There was I, wait-ing at the church, wait-ing at the church, wait-ing at the church. When I found he'd left me in the lurch,

Lor', how it did up - set me   All   at once he

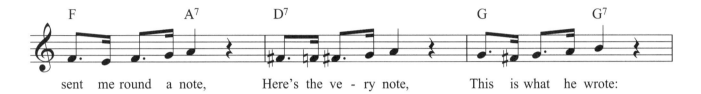

sent me round a note,   Here's the ve - ry note,   This is what he wrote:

"Can't get a-way to mar - ry you to- day,   My wife,   won't let me."

Verse 1

I'm in a nice bit of trouble, I confess;
Somebody with me has had a game.
I should by now be a proud and happy bride,
But I've still got to keep my single name.
I was proposed to by Obadiah Binks
In a very gentlemanly way;
Lent him all my money so that he could buy
a home,
And punctually at twelve o'clock to-day

Chorus

There was I, waiting at the church,
Waiting at the church;
When I found he'd left me in the lurch,
Lor', how it did upset me!
All at once, he send me round a note,
Here's the very note,
This is what he wrote:
"Can't get away to marry you today,
my wife, won't let me!"

Verse 2

Lor, what a fuss Obadiah made of me
When he used to take me in the park!
He used to squeeze me till I was
black and blue,
When he kissed me he used to leave a mark.
Each time he met me he treated me to port,
Took me now and then to see the play;
Understand me rightly, when I say he
treated me,
It wasn't him but me that used to pay.

Verse 3

Just think how disappointed I must feel,
I'll be off me crumpet very soon.
I've lost my husband—the one I never had!
And I dreamed so about the honeymoon.
I'm looking out for another Obadiah,
I've already bought the wedding ring
There's all my little fal-the-riddles packed up
in my box,
Yes, absolutely two of ev'rything.

Any collection of Music Hall songs that were good in their own day and still have the power to entertain would have to include Vesta Victoria's 'Waiting At The Church'. Nothing less than an evergreen anthem for bridal disappointment, it was one of several tunes that Vesta Victoria sang on the topic of being unlucky in love. In 'And Now We Have To Call Him Father' it is 'mother' who draws a young man's affections away from her daughter, so leading to an insufferable situation of embarrassment and resentment. In 'He Was A Good Kind Husband' the past tense of the title signals her quick passage from bride to widow. If Vesta Victoria's stage persona were ever psychoanalysed, it might be thought that she was forever trying to sublimate her feelings about the father who started this train of disappointment with his reluctance to get her a dog ('Daddy Wouldn't Buy Me A Bow Wow').

In 'Riding On A Motor Car' she manages to acquire a suitable young man as a husband but never gets as far as the much-anticipated honeymoon since they immediately have a crash and he is immobilised for months. A pattern is beginning to emerge here and it is one of interwoven comedy and pathos. Both are present in 'Waiting at the Church', which conjures its forlorn image even before the 'bride' begins her tale of a courtship that is not short of clues that the potentially bigamous Obadiah Binks did not sound like much of a catch in the first place. There seems to be more than a little desperation in her readiness always to have a ring at the ready should another potential bridegroom come along and this leads us to assume that she has somehow failed to learn by this experience, or more probably has elected not to.

It would be nice to report that Vesta Victoria was in real life more fortunate in love than she pretended to be on stage and indeed she may well have been. However, personal details of her adult life are hard to come by, although she did seem to have a late-blooming career revival in the 1930s when she re-recorded a number of her earlier successes. Popular both in the US and Britain she lived to the age of 77, dying in Hampstead, London in 1951.

Vesta Victoria, a specialist in bitter-sweet songs of disappointment, was once painted in performance at the Old Bedford Music Hall by the artist Walter Sickert.

TRUE

ROMANCE

Songs of
Hearts and Flowers

For all of its cheerful abrasiveness and scepticism, the Music Hall had plenty of room for sentimental love songs. 'Lily Of Laguna', for all its faults, is a love song pure and simple, as is the more down-to-earth 'He's Going To Marry Mary Ann'. So, strangely, is 'Cushie Butterfield' where the object of the singer's desire sounds so unappealing as to reassure us that this really must be love since nothing else could justify the attraction. The singer of 'Daisy Bell' appears to suffer from a harmless fetish which combines bicycles with intimacy, but again there are no grounds to question the sincerity of the emotion. 'Keep Your Feet Still, Geordie Hinney' features two men in a bed but the real subject is the singer's love for Mary Clark of whom he is trying to dream despite being repeatedly woken by Geordie's hyperactive feet.

CUSHIE BUTTERFIELD

Words by George Ridley. Music from Harry Clifton's 'Pretty Polly Perkins'.
Arranged by C.E. Catcheside-Warrington.
Version © Copyright: 1927, J.G. Windows, Ltd.

Moderato

Aa's a brok - en hair-ted keel - man and As's ower heed in luv Wiv a

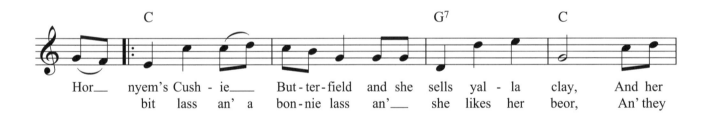

young lass in Gyet - sid and Aa caal her me duv.

Hor__ nyem's Cush - ie__ But-ter-field and she sells yal - la clay, And her
bit lass an' a bon-nie lass an'__ she likes her beor, An' they

1. *Chorus* **2.**

cous - in__ is a muck - man and they caall 'im Tom Gray.
caall her Cush-ie But - ter - field an' aa wish she was heor. She's a heor.

Verse 1

Aa's a broken hairted keelman and As's ower heed in luv
Wiv a young lass in Gyetsid and Aa call hor me duv.
Hor nyem's Cushie Butterfield and she sells yalla clay,
And her cousin is a muckman and they call 'im Tom Gray.

Chorus

She's a big lass an' a bonnie lass an' she likes hor beor,
An' they caall hor Cushie Butterfield and Aa wish she was heor.

Verse 2

Hor eyes is like two holes in a blanket bornt throo,
An' hor broos iv a mornin' wad spyen a yung coo,
An' when aa heer hor shoutin' — "Will ye buy only clay?"
Like a candyman's trumpet, it steals me yung hart away.

Verse 3

Ye'll oft see hor doon at Sangit when the fresh harrin comes in,
She's like a bagful o' saadust tied roond wiv a string;
She weers big galoshes tee, an' hor stockins once was white,
An 'hor bedgoon it's laelock, an' hor hat's nivver strite.

Verse 4

When Aa axed hor te marry us, she started te laff;
"Noo, nyen o' you monkey tricks, for Aa like nee sic chaff."
Then she started a' bubblin' an' roared like a bull,
An' the cheps on a Keel ses Aa's nowt but a fyuel.

Verse 5

She ses the chep 'et gets us 'ill heh te work ivvery day,
An' when he comes hyem at neets he'll heh to gan an' seek clay.
An' when he's away seekin't Aa'll myek baals an' sing,
O weel may the keel row that ma laddie's in.

Despite the capital's long shadow, Music Hall was by no means confined to London. There was a lively provincial tradition with one or two particularly vigorous strongholds. Many provincial performers migrated to London and although some adopted a neutral accent or tried to acquire a Cockney one, many, through choice or necessity, retained their provincial or national dialect. Notable among these was Lancashire's George Formby, Yorkshire's Tom Foy, and Scotland's Harry Lauder and Will Fyffe. Tyneside also produced its share of Music Hall writers amongst whom was George Ridley who penned the lyrics to 'Cushie Butterfield'. Matching his earthy lyric to the prim melody of Harry Clifton's 'Pretty Little Polly Perkins', Ridley created a Tyneside-accented keelman's hymn to what sounds like a very rough diamond indeed. Cushie Butterfield, portrayed waiting for the herring to come in, is a hoarse-voiced, tangle-haired, beer-drinking fishwife with eyes like two holes burned in a blanket and whose work clothes include off-white stockings, galoshes and a general sartorial effect that her lovestruck admirer likens to a bagful of sawdust tied around with string. Her appeal to the keelman seems entirely genuine if hard to fathom. The sudden incongruous mention of her lilac nightgown is either a hint at sexual intimacy or further evidence of a very uncertain dress sense when it comes to assembling her work wardrobe.

Although the song consciously trades in contrasts, deflation and ambiguity, in the end it remains a little confusing. We cannot quite work out what Cushie's reaction is to her admirer's mixture of affection and his decidedly ungallant description of her. The real strength of 'Cushie Butterfield' as a song lies partly in the uncompromising dialect in which it is written which conveys an authentic vigour of its own, and partly in the fact that it is obviously written with knowledge of the hardworking milieu of which it speaks. Nothing could stand in more stark contrast to 'Champagne Charlie' whose singer also hailed from Tyneside but who affected the personality of a wealthy metropolitan Londoner who revelled in a champagne-sodden fantasy life that betrayed nothing of his origins. Nor does Cushie come from the same world as pretty little Polly Perkins of Paddington Green—a capricious girl 'as beautiful as a butterfly and proud as a Queen' who turns down her milkman suitor not for a Viscount or an Earl but for a bus conductor. George Ridley's 'Cushie Butterfield' has survived to the present day and can occasionally be heard in ragged chorus at Newcastle United football matches.

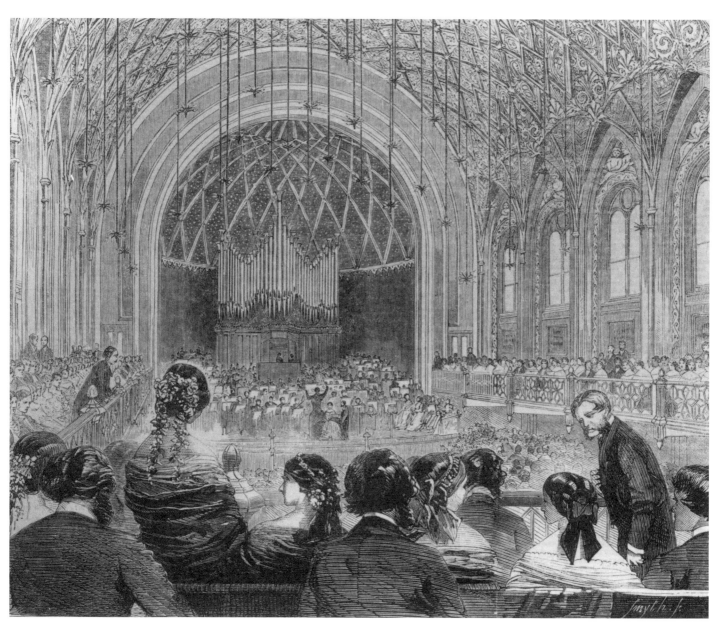

St. James's Music Hall.

DAISY BELL
(A BICYCLE MADE FOR TWO)

Sung by Katie Lawrence.

Words and Music by Harry Dacre.

Verse

There is a flower within my heart,
Daisy, Daisy!
Planted one day by a glancing dart,
Planted by Daisy Bell.
Whether she loves me or loves me not,
Sometimes it's hard to tell.
Still I am longing to share the lot
Of a beautiful Daisy Bell!

Chorus

Daisy, Daisy, give me your answer do!
I'm half crazy, all for the love of you!
It won't be a stylish marriage.
I can't afford a carriage,
But you'll look sweet upon the seat
Of a bicycle made for two.

American actress Rose Coghlan and friend on a bicycle built for two (c. 1885).

'Daisy Bell' was a hit of the 1890s made popular in Britain's halls by Katie Lawrence. She was a celebrated Music Hall singer who, through no fault of her own, became associated with both Walter Sickert (the wildly eccentric and possibly murderous artist who painted both her and Vesta Victoria) and James Joyce's notorious novel *Ulysses* in which a prostitute carries her name—probably not by coincidence, knowing Joyce's incisive memory and allusive tendencies.

Of at least 40 songs Lawrence helped to make well-known in her day, only 'Daisy Bell' became lastingly famous, infiltrating countless nooks and crannies of popular culture ever since. In 1964 it was the chosen debut number for the IBM 704, the first computer to sing. This in turn led to its similar use in Stanley Kubrick's 1968 film *2001: A Space Odyssey* when HAL the computer is being decommissioned. Other films as well as TV shows still feature it intermittently and it appeared on the B-side of Blur's single 'Sunday Sunday'. Allegedly the English songwriter Harry Dacre, on being charged duty to take his bicycle into the United States (a friend quipped that it was therefore fortunate he had not tried to take in a bicycle built for two which would have cost double), is said to have done what all good songwriters do and promptly made a hit out of one of life's little setbacks.

Enjoying more fame in the US after Jennie Lindsay triumphed with it at the Atlantic Garden in New York's Bowery district, the song went from strength to strength. In time it even provoked several answer songs, now with Daisy usually turning down her suitor, probably because the dawning age of the motor vehicle offered the more alluring prospect of young admirers with cars. Even so, Dacre's original song had offered an original take on the Victorian love song in which the image of a couple journeying through life together was neatly symbolised with the aid of a tandem.

HE'S GOING TO MARRY
MARY ANN Sung by Bessie Bellwood.

Words and Music by Joseph Tabrar.
© Copyright: Francis, Day & Hunter, Ltd.
All Rights Reserved. International Copyright Secured.

Allegretto

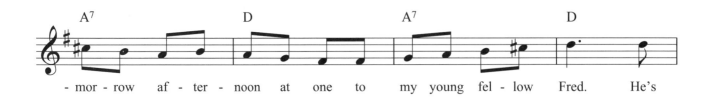

Oh, shout hoo-ray for Ma-ry Ann! I'm go-ing to get wed To-

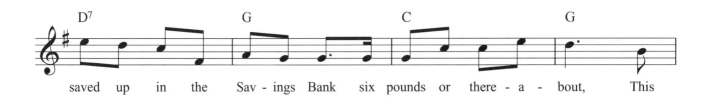

-mor-row af-ter-noon at one to my young fel-low Fred. He's

saved up in the Sav-ings Bank six pounds or there-a-bout, This

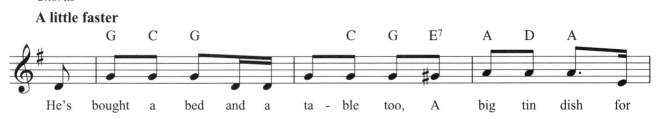

ve-ry day, to buy the home, He drew the mon-ey out.

Chorus

A little faster

He's bought a bed and a ta-ble too, A big tin dish for

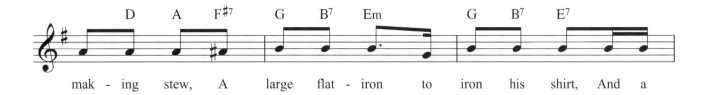

D   A   F#7   G   B7   Em   G   B7   E7

mak - ing stew, A large flat - iron to iron his shirt, And a

Am   A7   D7

flan - nel and a scrub - bing brush to wash a - way the dirt. And he's

G   C   Em   C   G   E7   Am

bought a pail and ba - sins three, A cof - fee pot, a ket - tle, and a

C   G

tea - pot for the tea, And a soap - bowl and a la - dle, And a

D7   G   C   D7

grid - iron and a cra - dle, And he's going to mar - ry Ma - ry

G   D7   Am   D7   G

Ann, that's *me!* He's going to ma - ry Ma - ry Ann!

Verse 1
Oh, shout hooray for Mary Ann!
I'm going to get wed
Tomorrow afternoon at one
To my young fellow, Fred.
He's saved up in the Savings Bank
Six pounds or thereabout,
This very day, to buy the home,
He drew the money out.

Chorus
He's bought a bed and a table too,
A big tin dish for making stew,
A large flatiron to iron his shirt,
And a flannel and a scrubbing brush to
Wash away the dirt.
And he's bought a pail and basins three,
A coffee pot, a kettle, and a teapot
for the tea,
And a soup bowl and a ladle,
And a gridiron and a cradle,
And he's going to marry Mary Ann, that's me!
He's going to marry Mary Ann!

Verse 2
My friends remark, "Oh, what a lark
To see the money fly!"
They say we're two young sillies, and
We don't know what to buy.
But just you leave my Fred alone,
He's such a knowing sort,
He lays the money out A-1,
And this is what he's bought.

Verse 3
He went right off to Maples, where
The furniture is grand,
He said he meant to have things new,
Not common second-hand.
We've got one chair, one table, and
One chest of drawers, two mugs,
Two plates, two cups, two saucers, and
A pair of water-jugs.

Mary Ann was a character who made an appearance in several Music Hall songs. She was a kind of easily recognisable young everywoman, chasing a man or more usually being chased by one. In this instance she seems to be seeking a stable relationship, personifying the excited bride-to-be who seems to have captured the heart of an agreeable if impetuous young man anxious to 'lay the money out' at Maples' furniture store. Associated with no particular singer, Mary Ann was simply part of the music hall landscape, as was the fictional and rather gormless John Willie who appeared in several of George Formby, Senior's songs. Bessie Bellwood sang 'He's Going To Marry Mary Ann' taking on the character herself and for once delivering a Music Hall number where everything seems to be going rather well for the happy couple, with no sign of deflation, irony or disaster in prospect. It was written by one of the halls' most prolific songwriters, Joseph Tabrar who created literally thousands of songs in his 60-year career. Perhaps the most famous was the novelty song 'Daddy Wouldn't Buy Me A Bow Wow', first sung by Vesta Victoria in 1892 and, rather less plausibly, by Peter Sellers and Helen Mirren in the rightly forgotten 1980 movie *The Fiendish Plot Of Dr. Fu Manchu*.

The folly of these 'two young sillies' excitedly splashing out on furniture and keen to avoid anything that might be seen as 'common second-hand', seems forgivable and bears no relation to the giddy excesses of Champagne Charlie, nor to the kind of trivial social impersonation that is 'Ria's downfall in Bessie Bellwood's 'Wotcher 'Ria'. Mary Ann and Fred's dream is a realisable one not only for them but also for the better-off in the audience. If 'He's Going To Marry Mary Ann' is not a great song, it is still a somehow charming one, concerned as it is with neither great poverty nor great wealth but with down-to-earth characters seeking to make a home for themselves. Maples, incidentally, carried on fulfilling the dreams of several generations of Mary Anns and Freds until 1997 when its internationally famous London flagship store at 149 Tottenham Court Road closed its doors for the last time.

KEEP YOUR FEET STILL, GEORDIE HINNEY

Words by Joe Wilson. Tune: 'Nellie Gray'. Arranged by C.E. Catcheside-Warrington.

Moderato

Wor___ Geor-die and Bob John-son byeth lay i' one___ bed In a

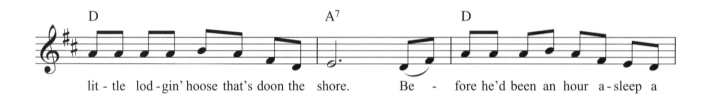

lit-tle lod-gin' hoose that's doon the shore. Be - fore he'd been an hour a-sleep a

kick from Geor-die's fut Made him wak-en up te roar i' stead o' snore.

Chorus

Keep yor feet still Geor-die Hin-ney let's be hap-py for the neet For Aa

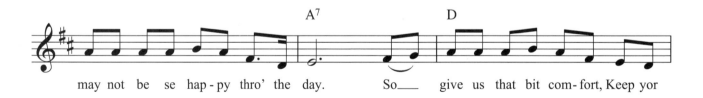

may not be se hap-py thro' the day. So___ give us that bit com-fort, Keep yor

feet still Geor-die lad And___ div-vent drive me bon-ny dreams a-way.

Verse 1

Wor Geordie and Bob Johnson byeth lay i' one bed
In a little lodgin' hoose that's doon the shore.
Before he'd been an hour asleep a kick from Geordie's fut
Made him waken up te roar i'stead o' snore.

Chorus

Keep yor feet still Geordie hinney let's be happy for the neet
For Aa may not be se happy thro' the day.
So give us that bit comfort, keep yor feet still Geordie lad
And divvent drive me bonny dreams away.

Verse 2

Aa dremt thor wes a dancin' held an' Mary Clark we there,
An' Aa thowt we tript it leetly on the floor,
An' Aa prest hor heevin' breest te mine when walsin' roond the room,
That's mair than Aa dor ivver de afore.

Verse 3

Ye knaa the lad she gans wi', they caall him Jimmy Green,
Aa thowt he tried te spoil us i' wor fun,
But Aa dremt Aa nailed 'im heavy, an' blacked the big feul's eyes,
If Aa'd slept its hard te tell what Aa wad deun.

Verse 4

Aa thowt Aa set hor hyem that neet; content we went alang,
Aa kissed hor lips a hundord times or mair,
An' Aa wisht the road wad nivor end, se happy like was Aa,
Aa cud waak a thoosand miles we' Mary there.

Verse 5

Aa dreamt Jim Green had left the toon an' left he's luv te me,
An Aa thowt the hoose wes foonished wi' the best,
An Aa dremt Aa just hed left the Chorch wi' Mary be me side,
When yor clumsy feet completely spoilt the rest.

ittle concession was made to London, the informal capital of Music Hall, by the Tyneside songwriter Joe Wilson. Wilson, born in 1841, made his money as a printer in Gateshead and wrote songs on the side, and he eventually became a defiantly local Music Hall artist. His dialect songs posed a severe obstacle to outsiders in the days when there were no broadcast media to introduce southerners to one of Britain's more unyielding local accents. His most durable lyric was 'Keep Your Feet Still, Geordie Hinney' which he set to the tune 'Nellie Gray' as arranged by C. E. Catcheside-Warrington. Wilson would die at the age of 33 but in his short life he not only found time for careers as printer, songwriter and performer but also became a Newcastle publican for a time. His most famous song had a life of its own and is not associated with any one performer other than Joe Wilson. 'Keep Your Feet Still, Geordie Hinney' fairly rattles along with its tale of two lads sharing a boarding house bed— a sufficiently common practice at the time to be devoid of sexual overtones—and Bob Johnson's recurring complaint that his romantic dream of Mary Clark keeps getting interrupted by Geordie's restless feet. ('Hinney' is not a surname as its capitalisation in the title might imply, but a local term of endearment derived from 'honey' and used regardless of gender rather like the Yorkshire 'love'. Geordie is only identified as 'our Geordie' rendered in the local dialect as 'Wor Geordie'). The song proceeds as an exercise in deferred gratification. Bob Johnson's dream pursuit of Mary Clark makes dogged but fitful progress as he is repeatedly woken and, not for the first time in a Music Hall song, *coitus* is of the *interruptus* variety. This time the wedding is a dreamed one but the disruption once more comes from Geordie's all too real feet.

LILY OF LAGUNA *Sung by Eugene Stratton.*

Words and Music by Leslie Stuart.

wants me,_____ yes, 'kase she wants me help her do de

call - in' and de count - in'. She plays her mu - sic_____ to call de

lone lambs_____ dat roam a - bove,_____ But I'm de black sheep and I'm

wait - ing For de sig - nal of ma lit - tle la - dy love.

Chorus

She's ma la - dy love,___ she is ma dove, ma ba - by love,

She's no gal for sit - tin' down to dream, She's de on - ly queen La - gu - na knows;

I know she likes me, I know she likes me be-kase she says so; She is de

Lil - y of La - gu - na, She is ma Lil - y and ma rose.

Verse 1

It's de same old tale of a palpatating nigger
Ev'ry time, ev'ry time;
It's de same old trouble of a coon
Dat wants to be married very soon;
It's de same old heart dat is longing for its lady
Ev'ry time, yes, ev'ry time,
But not de same gal, not de same gal.
She is ma Lily, ma Lily, ma Lily gal!
She goes ev'ry sundown, yes, ev'ry sundown
She goes ev'ry sundown, yes,
Ev'ry sundown callin' in de cattle up de mountain;
I go 'kase she wants me, yes,
'Kase she wants me help her do de call-in' and de countin'.
She plays her music to call de lone lambs dat roam above,
But I'm de black sheep and I'm waitin'
For de signal of ma little lady love.

Chorus

She's ma lady love, she is ma dove, ma baby love,
She's no gal for sittin' down to dream,
She's de only queen Laguna knows;
I know she likes me,
I know she likes me,
Bekase she says so;
She is de Lily of Laguna, she is ma Lily and ma Rose.

Verse 2

When I first met Lil it was down in old Laguna
At de dance, oder night;
So she says, "Say, a'm curious for to know
When ye leave here de way yer goin' to go,
'Kase a wants to see who de lady is
Dat claims ye all way home, way home to-night."
I says, "I've no gal, never had one."
And den ma Lily, ma Lily, ma Lily gal!
She says, "Kem't believe ye, a kern't believe ye,
Else I'd like to have ye shapperoon me;
Dad says he'll esscortch me, says he'll esscortch me,
But it's mighty easy for to lose him."
Since then each sundown I wander here and roam around
Until I know ma lady wants me,
Till I hear de music of de signal sound.

'Lily Of Laguna', an astonishingly popular song for much of the past hundred years, today looks like a minefield of potential offence and seems to have an internal logic purposely designed to baffle. Where exactly is this Italian- or Spanish-sounding Laguna that is the focus of the song? According to the lyric, the place appears to possess a dance hall, mountains, cattle and sheep, although this does not get us very far. We are left to conclude that the song must be set in the south-eastern states of America judging by its offensive portrait of 'the palpatating nigger' who features in it (and what is this word 'palpatating?'— dialect for 'palpitating'? If so, how might it sound different from the correctly spelled word?). For goodness' sake, who wrote this lyric and what was on his mind? Racial attitudes were very different in 1898 but surely simple logic existed more or less as it does now. Leslie Stuart was a British songwriter who, according to his biographer, Andrew Lamb, was evoking a village called Laguna which was populated by cave-dwelling Native Americans and situated somewhere in between New Orleans and California.

As a location this is vague to say the least, and the place anyway sounds wildly implausible. Perhaps we would do better to consider the song as an exercise in nostalgia set at a mythical time and in an artfully synthesised location. There is after all no evidence that Leslie Stuart ever visited the American south-east or south-west; if he did, it does not appear to have been a fact-finding trip. The true logic of his song's courtship between an African American and a Native American shepherdess(!) seems to be that Stuart wrote the song to be performed primarily by blackface singers whose cultural history stretched no further than the end of various British seaside piers; 'The World's Greatest Coon Song' says the cringeworthy strapline on the song's early sheet music. Laguna, it seems, was part of popular music's fantasy south that also contained Stephen Foster's magnolia-scented locations and was presumably peopled by who looked like Al Jolson singing about their Mammy, their Sonny Boy or the Swannee River. Foster, from Pennsylvania, only ever went south of the Mason Dixon line once and then very briefly, while Leslie Stuart was born near Liverpool and spent much of his life in and around Manchester.

'Lily Of Laguna' though, somehow caught the world's imagination. Its strolling rhythm and catchy tune suited the Music Hall perfectly. Everyone joined in with the chorus. Perhaps because both the words and the music were written by Stuart, it all fitted and flowed well.

Ethnically cleansed versions were recorded by Bing Crosby and Mary Martin among others, and the chorus could always be sung without the verses, so avoiding a lot of problems. 'She's My Lady Love' became a sort of informal title for this version. The now infamous *Black & White Minstrel Show* which flourished on BBC TV in the 1960s featured the song many times before the show was finally cancelled in 1978. By then the blackface element had been much reduced but the show rightly remained a source of embarrassment. 'Lily Of Laguna' is rarely heard now but, like many a Music Hall favourite, it has seeped into the collective consciousness in a way that some superior songs of its day somehow never managed to do.

MR EUGENE STRATTON

18/6/04.

THE FUTURE MRS 'AWKINS *Sung by Albert Chevalier.*

Words and Music by Albert Chevalier.
© Copyright: Reynolds & Co.
All Rights Reserved. International Copyright Secured.

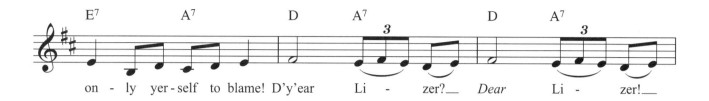

on - ly yer-self to blame! D'y'ear   Li - zer?__ *Dear*   Li - zer!__

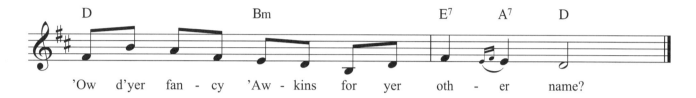

'Ow   d'yer   fan - cy   'Aw - kins   for   yer   oth - er   name?

Verse 1
I knows a little doner, I'm about to own 'er,
She's a goin' to marry me.
At fust she said she wouldn't, then she
said she couldn't,
Then she whispered, "Well, I'll see."
Sez I, "Be Missis 'Awkins, Missis 'En'ry 'Awkins,
Or acrost the seas I'll roam.
So 'elp me Bob I'm crazy, Lizer
you're a daisy,
Won't yer share my 'umble 'ome?"
(*Spoken or sung*) "Won't yer?"

Chorus
Oh! Lizer! Sweet Lizer!
If yer die an old maid you'll 'ave only
yerself to blame!
D'y'ear Lizer? Dear Lizer!
'Ow d'yer fance 'Awkins for yer other name?

(The last line of the last chorus runs:
Missis 'En'ry 'Awkins is a fus-class name.)

Verse 2
I shan't forgit our meetin', "G'arn"
was 'er greetin'
"Just yer mind wot you're about."
'Er pretty 'ead she throws up, then she turns
'er nose up,
Sayin', "Let me go, I'll shout!"
"I like your style" sez Lizer, thought as I'd
surprise 'er,
Cops 'er round the waist like this!
Sez she, "I must be dreamin', chuck it, I'll
start screamin',"
"If yer do," sez I, "I'll kiss"—
(*Spoken or sung*) "Now then!"

Chorus

Albert Chevalier was not of the Music Hall, nor did he ever feel himself to belong there. He is that rarity in the pre-WWI halls, an outsider from the middle class, yet he seemed able, as few Cockney comedians were, to understand and express that way of life. It is true that there is an element of idealisation in the Cockney world of his songs, but at his best he is able to get to its roots in a way that is only very rarely found in any other songs of this kind. He had been a straight actor in the years between 1877 and 1901 when his move into Music Hall was prompted by necessity—a lack of acting work. He was an immediate success despite his misgivings that he was not loud enough or lively enough for the halls. 'The Future Mrs 'Awkins' was one of the songs he sang on his very first Music Hall appearance. The others were 'Knocked 'Em in the Old Kent Road', 'Coster's Serenade', 'Funny Without Being Vulgar' and 'The Hasty Way 'E Sez It'. He wrote most of his own lyrics although his brother Charles Ingle supplied some of the music. John Crook, who wrote the melody for 'Jeerusalem's Dead!' may also have written the music for 'The Future Mrs 'Awkins' although here no one else is credited apart from Chevalier as the lyricist. Chevalier's association with the world of the legitimate drama, his recitals and especially the fact that he could never bring himself wholly to embrace the world of the halls, inevitably distanced him a little from many of his colleagues. Yet among his working-class Cockney numbers are to be found some of the best 'songs from the heart' of the Music Hall. The verse of 'The Future Mrs 'Awkins' may be spoken or sung and this option is not untypical; Chevalier's long experience of recital made him fond of the spoken element where the music adds texture but is not necessarily paired with the words. It has to be said that songs of pathos and sentiment, even if taken seriously in their day, usually seem comically exaggerated to later generations. There is the parallel example of the early days of American country music where bleak songs about dying infants, natural disasters, drunken killer husbands and other tragedies were also sincerely intended but now sound to be almost self-parodic in their unremitting gloom. However, when Music Hall sentiment is well-expressed within a comic framework as in 'The Future Mrs 'Awkins', genuine sincerity artfully blended with wry comedy makes a more plausible appeal to the sort of listener who cannot otherwise take the heart without the art. This internal conflict of tone is what makes a song like 'The Future Mrs 'Awkins' able to appeal outside its own time and beyond its first intended audience.

Albert Chevalier,
dressed in his familiar costermonger's attire.

Lust

and

INNUENDO

Songs About Sex

Since Victorian and Edwardian songs about sex necessarily had to rely on *double entendres* and suggestiveness, it follows that many of them were exceptionally inventive. Even so, some of them still sound tame today although contemporary audiences were quick—perhaps eager—to put sexual readings on the most innocent phrases once it was clear what the subject of the song was. This selection touches on one or two popular Music Hall scenarios: mixed bathing; the provocative promenade; the guarding of virginity presented as a long campaign; suggestive body language; and the desirability of the New Woman who, to the female singer's alarm, affects many male accoutrements. Since this last song was most famously performed by a man in drag claiming that he preferred to cling to his femininity, it is clear that the late Victorian view of sexuality was sometimes far from untroubled.

AND HER GOLDEN HAIR WAS HANGING DOWN HER BACK

Sung by Alice Leamar and Sir Seymour Hicks.

Words and Music by Felix McGlennon.
© Copyright: Francis, Day & Hunter, Ltd., and Trustees of the Felix McGlennon estate.
All Rights Reserved. International Copyright Secured.

Moderato

There was once a coun-try maid-en came to Lon-don for a trip, And her

gold-en hair was hang-ing down her back;____ She was wea-ry of the coun-try so she

gave her folks the slip, And her gold-en hair was hang-ing down her back;____ It was

once a vi-vid au-burn but her ri-vals called it red, So she

thought she could be hap-pier with an-oth-er shade in-stead. And she

stole the wash-ing so-da and ap-plied it to her head, And some

gold-en hair came stream-ing down her back.____

Chorus

But oh! Flo! Such a change you know, When she left the vil-lage she was shy;___ But a - las and a-lack! She's gone back With a naugh - ty lit - tle twin - kle in her eye!___

Verse 1
There was once a country maiden came to London for a trip,
And her golden hair was hanging down her back;
She was weary of the country so she gave her folks the slip,
And her golden hair was hanging down her back;
It was once a vivid auburn but her rivals called it red,
So she thought she could be happier with another shade instead.
And she stole the washing soda and applied it to her head,
And some golden hair came streaming down her back.

Chorus
But oh! Flo! such a change you know,
When she left the village she was shy;
But alas and alack! she's gone back
With a naughty little twinkle in her eye!

Verse 2
She had a country accent and a captivating glance,
And her golden hair was hanging down her back;
She wore some little diamonds that came from sunny France
And her golden hair was hanging down her back;
She wandered out in London for a breath of ev'ning air,
And strayed into a Palace that was fine and large and fair—
It might be in a Circus or it might be in a Square,
But her golden hair was hanging down her back. ▶

Verse 3

And London people were so nice to artless little Flo,
When her golden hair was hanging down her back;
That she had been persuaded to appear in a tableau
Where her golden hair was hanging down her back;
She posed beside a marble bath upon some marble stairs,
Just like a water nymph or an advertisement for Pears,
And if you ask me to describe the costume that she wears—
Well, her golden hair is hanging down her back.

Verse 4

She met a young philanthropist, a friend of Missus Chant,
And her golden hair was hanging down her back;
He lived in Peckham Rye with an extremely maiden aunt
Who had not a hair a-hanging down her back;
The lady looked upon him in her fascinating way,
And what the consequences were, I really cannot say,
But when his worthy maiden aunt remarked his coat next day,
Well, some golden hairs were hanging down the back.

Seymour Hicks.

One of the traditional ways of raising a laugh in the Music Hall was by the use of innuendo—an indirect observation usually suggesting but not explicitly stating something erotic, mean or derogatory. Innuendo was not by any means new nor was it confined to the lower dramatic arts, having been a staple of Elizabethan plays where it was commonplace some 400 years earlier, often in reference to sexual matters. In the Music Hall, precisely what was to be assumed by a given piece of innuendo was supposedly left to the imagination of the audience, although this pretence was clearly disingenuous. In later years Max Miller would push this practice to breaking point and beyond. By setting up an imminent rhyme he would lead an audience to expect a blue joke, but would rely on being interrupted by the loud laughter of the audience before he had to articulate the offensive word. Alternatively a contrived innocent rhyme would at the last minute replace the expected one, fooling no one. Miller would then feel free to upbraid the audience for having dirty minds and giving him a bad name. Yet before Miller coarsened this technique, innuendo could often be presented more gently and teasingly on the halls. 'And Her Golden Hair Was Hanging Down Her Back' is a case in point.

The song, written by Felix McGlennon, was originally sung by Alice Leamar, but then it was taken from the Music Hall context by Sir Seymour Hicks and sung in over 500 performances in the musical *The Shop Girl,* which ran at London's Gaiety Theatre through 1894 and 1895. It is one of many songs that tell the story of the innocent maiden—in this case Flo—who comes to the great city and faces its perils. Marie Lloyd sang several such songs but this one rises above the mundane for several reasons. It makes skilful use of the repetition of the refrain, which is sometimes descriptive and sometimes suggestive. There is a charming adaptability to this golden hair (which got that way by Flo's judicious use of washing soda on her naturally red tresses) and becomes in turns, a striking asset, an aid to modesty, and the source of a tell-tale strand on the back of a man's jacket. McGlennon's lyric also makes coy reference to a late Victorian advertisement for Pears soap which showed a naked child and therefore identifies Flo's theatrical debut as being part of a nude tableau. The mention of 'Missus Chant' references Laura Ormiston Chant, a contemporary social reformer who wrote and lectured on social purity, temperance, and women's rights. The fact that the young philanthropist of the final verse is a friend of hers suggests that his implied sexual dalliance with Flo is a typical example of Victorian male hypocrisy: public virtue leavened with private vice.

AT MY TIME OF LIFE

Sung by Herbert Campbell.

Words and Music by T.W. Connor.

Allegretto

Now ev - er since I tied the knot, and which it ain't a

day, I've sat - is - fied my hus - band in my good old - fash - ioned

way. But since he's seen a gal in "bags", it's knocked him sure as

fate. He says I ain't worth that, be - cause I am *not* up to date.___

Chorus

There was none o' yer "High - ty Fligh - ty" girls, yer "Hi - Tidd - ly

Hi - ty" girls, When my old "Stick - in - the - mud"

took me for a wife. Now fan - cy me a -

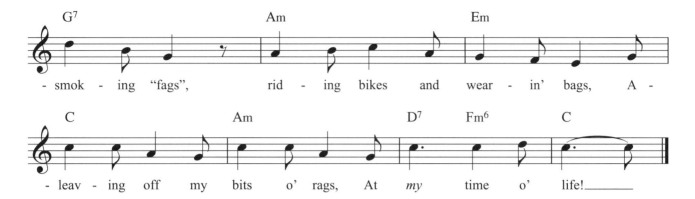

- smok - ing "fags", rid - ing bikes and wear - in' bags, A -

- leav - ing off my bits o' rags, At *my* time o' life!_____

Verse 1

Now ever since I tied the knot, and which it ain't a day,
I've satisfied my husband in my good old-fashioned way.
But since he's seen a gal in "bags", it's knocked him, sure as fate.
He says I ain't worth that, because I am not up to date.

Chorus

There was none o' yer "Highty Flighty" girls, yer "Hi-Tiddley Hi-ty" girls,
When my old "Stick-in-the-mud" took me for a wife.
Now fancy me a-smoking "fags", riding bikes and wearin' bags,
A-leaving off my bits o' rags at my time o' life!

Verse 2

I like my drop o' "stimulant" as all good ladies do,
A 'arf a quarten, "two out", used to do between the two;
But now he says it's only "roughs" as patronises "pubs",
For all "new Women" wot is "class" belongs to swagger clubs!

Chorus

There was none o' yer "Highty Flighty" girls, yer "Hi-Tiddley Hi-ty" girls,
When my old "Thing-a-my-bob" took me for a wife.
Now fancy me old "Mother Scrubs" a-jine-ing these "ere Totties" clubs.
Fancy me deserting "pubs" at my time o' life!

Verse 3

He'd like to see me got up with a cigarette to puff;
A "dickey dirt" and tie (as if I wasn't guy enough!)
Says I'd look well in "bloomers" and a "call-me-Charlie" hat!
If I'd proposed it he'd 'a said, "Get out, yer gay old cat!"

Chorus

There was none o' yer "Highty Flighty" girls, yer "Hi-Tiddley Hi-ty" girls,
When my old "Fourpenny-bit" took me for a wife.
Now fancy me a sportin' shirts! Playing billiards, backing "certs"
A-goin' about without my skirts at my time o' life!

A minefield of sexual politics and fertile ground for Freudian interpretations, 'At My Time Of Life' is a 'dame' song, and it was sung by Herbert Campbell, half of what was once a legendary pantomime team with Dan Leno. Both were known for playing dames and Campbell appeared in the Drury Lane pantomime for 22 years, for the last 14 of which he was partnered by Leno. Two of the weird conventions of British pantomime are that the leading male part is played by a young and shapely female and that the dame (in this context a comic old woman usually of generous proportions) is played by a male comedian.

Herbert Campbell.

The dame tradition is a curious one that echoes the *travesti* convention in opera, and in Music Hall it was long accepted as nothing more than innocent dressing up. Today it is hard not to sense an undercurrent of something murkier in the implication that a good-looking young woman can get away with anything— even playing a man—without ridicule, while an older woman must necessarily be a grotesque who needs to be crudely overplayed by a man. Were audiences satisfied with the extended one-note joke of a man pretending to be a woman? Or might it be that when Herbert Campbell or Dan Leno waggled their hips they were making fun of effeminate behaviour in a strait-laced age that happily indulged drag acts but dared not speak the name of homosexual ones? 'At My Time Of Life' is a Music Hall song that bounces off the dame tradition at a strange angle without really having anything else to do with pantomime other than the association with Herbert Campbell. Its strange logic pits an earthy traditional view of what a 'real' woman should be like against the fashionable allure of the New Women who affect aspects of men's mannerisms and behaviour—smoking, cycling, playing billiards, wearing shirts and trousers.

'I've satisfied my husband in my good old-fashioned way' sings this traditional woman…who in this case is actually a 19-stone man in drag. There is one brief nudge-and-wink contained in the line about what the singer's husband would like 'her' to wear: 'A 'dickey dirt' (shirt) and tie (as if I wasn't guy enough!)' but otherwise subtlety is conspicuous by its absence in this particular transgender song. Pantomime lingers on in Britain, still mixing sexual allusions with male/female role reversal and presenting the show mainly as a children's entertainment with smutty innuendo for the grown-ups. 'At My Time Of Life' is of special interest for its rich collection of contemporary slang: 'bags' for 'trousers', 'dickey dirt' for shirt, 'bloomers' for the garment advocated by Amelia Bloomer to allow emancipated women more freedom, 'fags' for cigarettes and 'certs' for racing certainties. All the slang words were fairly new, as was the notion of women's rights of which the mocked 'New Woman' was seen as a symptom. In his day, Herbert Campbell was famous for ridiculing what seemed to him to be taken too seriously. Today we might wonder if 'At My Time Of Life' might not have taken a little more seriously what it ridiculed.

EVERY LITTLE MOVEMENT

Sung by Marie Lloyd.

Words and Music by K. Hoschna and O.A. Haverbach.

Verse 1
Up to the West End, right in the best end,
Straight from the country came Miss Maudie Brown,
Father a curate, but couldn't endure it,
That's why the lady's residing in town.
Twelve months ago her modest self felt quite sublime
To sit on a fellow's knee who's been in all the grime!
And if you should want a kiss,
She'd droop her eyes like this,
But now she droops them just one at a time.

Chorus
And every little movement has a meaning of its own,
Every little movement tells a tale.
When she walks in dainty hobbles,
At the back round here, there's a kind of wibble-wobble;
And she glides like this,
Then the Johnnies follow in her trail,
'Cos when she turns her head like so,
Something's going, don't you know,
Every little movement tells a tale.

Verse 2
Down by the blue sea, cute as she could be,
Maudie would go for her dip every day.
Maudie has an eye for the boys, Oh my!
And it happens that Reggie was passing that way.
When Reggie saw her he fell into a trance,
He too is going bathing for here now, here's a chance.
She didn't smile or frown,
Just threw her signal down!
Then slyly shrugged her shoulders with a glance.

Chorus
And every little movement has a meaning of its own,
Every little movement tells a tale.
When she dashed into the ocean,
Reggie kept close by for to know her
Maudie tried to swim:
"Oh I'm here", said Reggie, "if you fail",
And in less than half a wink,
Maudie dear commenced to sink,
Every little movement tells a tale.

▶

Verse 3

Congratulations, such celebrations,
Bertie and Gertie have just tied the knot.
Both at the party, all gay and hearty,
And noticed the bridegroom looks anxious, eh
what?
When friends and relatives depart their different
ways,
Alone with the girlie of his heart.
And once again he turned the lights down low,
She looked at him like so,
Then shyly with her wedding ring she played.

Chorus

And every little movement has a meaning
of its own,
Every little movement tells a tale.
When alone no words they utter,
But when midnight chimed, then their hearts
begin to flutter.
And she yawned like this,
And stretches out her arm so frail,
And her hubby full of love,
Looks at her and points above,
Every little movement tells a tale.

Marie Lloyd dressed up to the nines.

Neither in print music form nor as recordings do Marie Lloyd's songs go very far towards suggesting how immensely popular she was. Typically 'Every Little Movement' (an American song by K. Hoschna and O. A. Haverbach) reveals a wholehearted acceptance of relations between the sexes. There are no layers of Victorian coyness here but neither are there any deeper insights into Marie Lloyd's background, nor anything more than a superficial observation of the kind of life she describes. In fact her songs rarely create a richly detailed imaginative world of their own like those of Gus Elen, nor do they take pleasure in playing with language as did so many Music Hall songs. An exception is 'My Old Man Said Follow The Van', also included here, where the catalogue of furniture and belongings gives a whiff of reality to a disorganised move of premises. Generally though, we are left to conclude from Marie Lloyd's choice of songs that the decision was often made on the basis of their being vessels that depended on her presence to fill them up and give them life.

Just as the film director Alfred Hitchcock was indifferent to literary merit when searching for books on which to base a film (he only wanted a plot, as he would do the rest), Marie Lloyd wanted a song through which to project her persona and her engagingly laissez-faire attitude towards sex.

'Every Little Movement' is one such song. It begins with the tale of Maudie Brown, a curate's daughter and her amorous adventures when she leaves home for the big city; but then, rather abruptly, it shifts gear and turns its focus upon Bertie and Gertie whose names vaguely suggest the milieu of Champagne Charlie and the bright young things of his generation. However 'Every Little Movement' does succeed in evoking some kind of seductive dream world in which sexual signals abound. This alone makes it interesting as a song and Marie Lloyd gave it her usual amiably lascivious reading, clearly relishing images like newly wed Gertie playing with her wedding ring to signal that it is time for bed.

I'VE NEVER LOST MY LAST TRAIN YET

Sung by Marie Lloyd.

Words by George Rollit. Music by George Le Brunn.
© Copyright: Bowerman & Co.
All Rights Reserved. International Copyright Secured.

Allegretto

day and in the dark, I have nev - er lost my last train

yet, oh no! I have nev - er lost my last train yet!

Verse 1

I'm a modest little maiden from the country,
Where I'm living with my mother quite alone;
And it's only very seldom she allows me
To betake myself to London "on my own":
For in town I have a sort of second cousin,
Who enjoys to take me round to see the sights;
And he always comes and meets me
At the station and he treats me
To the various Metropolitan delights.

Chorus

Yes, there's nothing half so sweet
As the days on which we meet,
For he's quite the nicest boy I've ever met;
But although I love a lark
In the day and in the dark,
I have never lost my last train yet, Oh No!
I have never lost my last train yet!

Verse 2

I admit I'm very fond of nature's beauty,
Of the flowers and the birdies in the air,
And the chickens and the ducks who
gather round me,
And the cattle who regard me with a stare;
Now this sort of thing, no doubt
is very charming,
But it's really getting very, very slow,
And I'm longing for sensations,
Such as gentle dissipations,
Which I always find in London when I go.

Chorus

For I've experienced what it is
To have quaffed a glass of "fiz",
When you're supping with a gay and giddy set,
And I've joined with one and all
In a Covent Garden ball,
But I've never lost my last train yet, Oh No!
I have never lost my last train yet.

Verse 3

Now although I am as heartless as a lambkin
That has never heard of mint sauce in its "puff",
I am getting somewhat sick of rural beauty,
Or in other words I've had about enough.
I should love to have a flat in Piccadilly
And to go and do exactly as I choose
For had I my habitation
In a West End situation,
Then of course, I would not have a train to lose.

Chorus

Yes, I've learnt to know the bliss
Of a stolen little kiss,
When you heave a sigh and softly murmer,
"Pet!"
As you gaze into his face,
Wrapt in amorous embrace,
But I've never lost my last train yet, Oh No!
I've never lost my last train yet.
▶

Verse 4

Now a week or two ago I asked my cousin
To escort me to Boulogne—just for the day;
Very soon we were on board
the Marguerite, boys,
And we had a fair old beano on the way.
At Boulogne we found the fun was
fast and furious,
And of ways to pass the time there was no lack;
We were feeling, oh so happy,
When I said, "Look here, old chappy,
Don't you think it's time that we were
getting back?"

Chorus

For when looking at the clock
I received a dreadful shock,
On discovering that the sun had gone and set.
So a telegram I wrote:
"Dear Mama, I've missed the boat!"
But I haven't lost my last train yet, Oh No!
I haven't lost my last train yet.

This sustained *double entendre* from Marie Lloyd has its admirers although the title phrase somehow sounds rather awkward. Did anyone ever talk of 'losing' a train when they missed it? Probably not and it certainly sounds very odd now. The word is used to hammer home what is really meant: I haven't lost my virginity yet. With that out of the way we are left with a litany of racy metropolitan adventures enjoyed by the innocent country girl in the company of a man who clearly seeks to promote himself from her 'sort of second cousin' to her sort of first lover. The song might be better if it didn't have so much in it about the limited appeal of the countryside. This is not really necessary since we quickly get the message that our chaste heroine is sick of rural beauty and would much rather have a flat in Piccadilly. Instead she has to keep telling us in different picturesque ways that she prefers the city and that every day-return trip she makes to London has its built-in curfew: the last train which, as long as it is not 'lost', symbolically assures us her virtue remains intact. Furthermore she seems to imply that if she had the sort of London flat she craves, the question of losing her virginity would no longer be relevant. Did they write that sort of thing into the lease? This shift from the railway system to property rental as analogy for a girl's moral progress threatens to overwhelm a trite song. Anyway George Rollit's lyric seems a bit underpowered and certainly too elliptical for no-nonsense Marie Lloyd, who tackled the same sort of thing rather more breezily in 'What Did She Know About Railways?' This was yet another song about a farmer's daughter coming to the city and all the attendant risks she meets. Apropos her midnight arrival at Euston Station these bracingly direct lines appear: 'The guards and the porters came round her by the score/And she told them all that she'd never had her ticket punched before.' This somehow sounds more like Marie Lloyd who no doubt, even here, felt the need to reinforce the blatant innuendo with a huge stage wink.

THE SWIMMING MASTER Sung by Dan Leno.

Words and Music by Herbert Darnley.
© Copyright: Bowerman & Co.
All Rights Reserved. International Copyright Secured.

Allegro moderato

When the wa-ter is wet and the air is dry A beau-ti-ful sight you may then es-py, On the pier in the sum-mer-time there am I Teach-ing the la-dies to swim____ Though fright-ened at first of the wa-ter they be, Their con-fi-dence soon will re-turn, don't you see, When they have feast-ed their eyes up-on me, And no-ticed my fig-ure so trim____

Chorus

As I teach the girls to float____ the sea goes down each throat____ They say, "Oh Dear! I'm going to sink," I have them up with a charm-ing wink. To my

man - ly chest they cling_____ and their arms a - round me fling,

Oh dear what a time I have when I teach the girls to swim._____

Verse 1

When the water is wet and the air is dry
A beautiful sight you may then espy,
On the pier in the summer-time there am I
Teaching the ladies to swim.
Though frightened at first of the water they be,
Their confidence soon will return, don't you see,
When they feasted their eyes upon me,
And noticed my figure so trim.

Patter

You didn't notice my figure when I first appeared—I came on
you too suddenly. You weren't able to grasp me altogether, as
it were—I'll go off and come on again. (Retires off and
re-enters) There! Now you can notice me properly. You see
you've got a north-east view of me. It is really remarkable
the effect I leave on people who see me for the first time.
When I walked on the pier last Monday, two ladies looked at
me and fell over into the water. I nearly got the Victoria Cross
For that. Of course, that was my chance. The moment
I saw the ladies in the water, quick as thought, I made one dash
To where they tied the boat up; untied the boat, got in, and pulled out.
▶

But I was just too late. The ladies could swim and they were saved. But it was a marvellous escape. If I'd saved them I'd have got the medal. There was an old man, a very old man, all bearded and wrinkled, lying asleep on the sand. I was up on top, on the pr-pro-prom, on the pier. I dashed down before anybody could stop me, seized the old man, grabbed him by the legs, up on to the gravel and on to the pavement. Saved his life. There's not the slightest doubt if he had stayed there asleep till the tide come up, he'd have been drowned.

Chorus
As I teach the girls to float, the sea goes down each throat.
They say, "Oh Dear! I'm going to sink,"
I have them up with charming wink.
To my manly chest they cling and their arms around me fling,
Oh dear what a time I have when I teach girls to swim.

Verse 2
My position is one of a deal of trust,
I'm so full of secrets I feel I could bust,
For the way some girls make up's enough to disgust—
Still not a soul I've told
You would be surprised if some girls you could see,
Whose figures you think are from blemish quite free,
Why, do you know—that is—well, between you and me—
Oh! I could a tale unfold.

Patter
I could tell you things you'd hardly believe—in fact, I could tell you things I don't believe myself. There was a strange lady come to me the other day and said, "Do you mind my swimming with my stockings on?" I said, "No." Well, out she ran, dived in, and came up feet first—there she was bobbing up and down—I didn't know she'd got a cork leg. Another lady asked me what I'd charge to teach her to swim. I said, "One Guinea." She said, "Alright, I shan't be long," and went into the dressing room, a fine strapping figure. When she came out, I didn't know her. I said, "I'll only charge you half a guinea, 'cos there's only half of you to teach." ▶

Chorus

Both the single and married I teach to dive;
The single young girls can sometimes contrive
To swim under water while I'm counting five;
That's quite a record I call.
But Oh! I've tried, but I've found it in vain,
For diving the sweet married ladies to train.
They under the water can never remain,
They can't keep their mouths shut at all.

Patter

You wouldn't believe how strong you get having so much to do with water. Before I taught swimming I was a poor, weak little chap, with no chest and thin arms. Well, now look at me! Oh, I love the water; all our family love water—I've seen my father drink quarts of water—of course, with something in it. And my brother, he's passionately fond of water—he's a milkman. (*Turning as though to someone who has just entered*) "Good morning, Miss Winkle, good morning! Beautiful day indeed. Yes'm, ready if you are. Well I never! What a pretty bathing dress! Made it yourself! Ah! Don't you think you might have made a little more of it while you were at it? It won't shrink! Well, I hope not. Now then, ready—one, two, three, go! You dived rather lumpy. That's right—don't struggle—keep cool. Don't talk, you mustn't drink the water. Take nice quiet strokes—one, two, three my dinner's at four, five, six. Keep your head up—head up! No! keep that under. There! I knew that dress wouldn't last—here's a pin."

Chorus

This Dan Leno number marks another addition to the Music Hall's roll-call of songs about the hidden agenda of men teaching girls to swim. We should remind ourselves that Victorian mores had prescribed everyday female clothing that might suggest form but most comprehensively disguised flesh. Edwardian times brought a lighter spirit yet the social opportunities for a man having close physical contact with a flimsily garbed woman outside of marriage or the brothel were rare. Teaching swimming offered one of those opportunities. We should not perhaps make too much of the fact that the brilliant librettist William S. Gilbert would die in the spring of 1911 while giving a swimming lesson to two local girls in the lake of his Harrow home Grim's Dyke. When one of his charges lost her footing, Gilbert dived to save her, but suffered a fatal heart attack in the middle of the lake. He was 74 and a man of such generous and open spirit (sometimes admittedly disguised beneath an irascible professional manner) that there is no reason to suppose that his motives were as devious as those of the singer of 'The Swimming Master', a song Gilbert had probably heard. The patter to this song is classic Dan Leno. The opening is confident and winning, yet it remains difficult to pin down quite what gives it its appeal. Leno just gives the impression that he knows how to work an audience and whether his lines are quirkily fanciful or just simple and obvious comic observations, he sounds as if he is greatly at home on stage. Leno possessed an extraordinary talent for extracting wonderment and surprise out of the obvious. It was a talent that long foreshadowed much more recent comics. They too trade on the everyday humour of recognition that makes us laugh in the same way we might if we were to catch an unexpected glimpse of ourselves in a mirror and start to pass judgement on what for a moment we imagine is someone else. 'The Swimming Master', like 'The Huntsman', reveals Leno's capacity to word-paint.

Audiences would laugh at the conceit that this slight individual is now boasting a far more robust torso than he used to possess. What could he have looked like before? They would enjoy the anecdote of his father drinking quarts of water (the information is that the water had something else in it comes, significantly, afterwards). At the end of the patter we find one of Leno's most successful techniques: conjuring characters not by describing them but through his own reactions to them. Leno's link with the audience is thus strengthened as the audience's own responses are necessarily mediated by his own.

Dan Leno.

WHEN I TAKE MY MORNING PROMENADE

Sung by Marie Lloyd.

Words and Music by A.J. Mills and Bennett Scott.
© Copyright: B. Feldman & Co., Ltd.
All Rights Reserved. International Copyright Secured.

Allegretto

As I take my morn-ing prom-e-nade, Quite a fash-ion card, on the

prom-e-nade. Now I don't mind nice boys star-ing hard If it

sat-is-fies their de-sire. Do you think my dress is

a lit-tle bit, Just a lit-tle bit not too much of it? If it

shows my shape just a lit-tle bit, That's the lit-tle bit the boys ad-mire.

Verse 1

Since Mother Eve in the Garden long ago,
Started the fashion, fashion's been a fashion.
She wore a strip that has mystified the priests,
Still every season brought a change of green.
She'd stare if she came to town,
What would Mother Eve think of my new
Parisian gown.

Chorus

As I take my morning promenade,
Quite a fashion card, on the promenade.
Now I don't mind nice boys staring hard
If it satisfies their desire.
Do you think my dress is a little bit,
Just a little bit not too much of it?
If it show my shape just a little bit,
That's the little bit the boys admire.

Verse 2

Fancy the girls in the prehistoric days
Had to wear a bearskin to cover up their fair skin.
Lately Salome has danced to be sure,
Wearing just a row of beads and not much more.
Fancy me dressing like that, too!
I'm sure *The Daily Mirror* man would want
An interview.

Verse 3

I've heard that grandmother wore a crinoline;
Then came the bustle—Oh! Wasn't that a tussle.
Women were tied up and loaded up with dress,
But fashion now decrees that she must wear much less.
Each year her costume grows more brief,
I wonder when we'll get back to the good
Old-fashioned leaf.

Marie Lloyd is well represented in this collection. In part this is because she lays some claim to being the greatest Music Hall performer of them all. It is, of course, a matter of taste, yet Marie Lloyd, like George Formby, Sr, seemed to have the knack of personifying someone whose intrinsically attractive personality was projected through a repertoire of songs that suited her down to the ground. Of course those songs were artfully chosen to do just that, but what audiences really wanted to hear was not this or that new song—they wanted to see Marie Lloyd projecting herself through those numbers, live, on stage. She was warm, feisty and sexy, and each song reinforced those qualities to some degree.

Often accused of being too risqué, she perhaps attracted censure from society's more unforgiving commentators simply because she was a woman. Even her most salty lyrics were outdone by those of some male performers, so perhaps she was seen to be challenging the perceived wisdom that sexual innuendo might be appropriate coming from men but it was unseemly coming from women. Additionally there were sometimes shades of propriety separating local audiences at venues sometimes only a few miles apart. For example, an East End audience such as the one that once gave Lloyd a rough time (despite being itself steeped in poverty, vice and corporeality) was perhaps more conservative in its views about women's public behaviour than the audience of a West End Music Hall.

Marie Lloyd (left), the heroine of the halls.

'When I Take My Morning Promenade' treads a typically teasing fine line, rejoicing in the figure of a shapely woman out taking her morning stroll. The words are innocent enough, although the tone of the song is deliberately provocative, paying lip service to the promenade as a notional display of fashion awareness but not shying away from the fact that female fashion itself was intended to assist in provoking a sexual response.

Although Lloyd presents herself in this song as a caricature of a fashion-conscious society lady, she makes it clear that as far as she is concerned fashionable clothes are not just modish affectations, they are accoutrements intended to accentuate those parts of the female body that attract men. In an oblique way, this is another example of that old Music Hall staple, deflation. By hinting that the society lady's sartorial pretensions in fact mask earthier appetites, Marie Lloyd, the heroine of the halls, expresses a more honest approach to the real purpose of the promenade. Similarly, Chevalier, Formby Sr., and Elen were able to reflect audiences' gut feelings back to them and in doing so also achieved a kind of folk art that distinguished them from those more sophisticated theatre entertainers who simply diverted their middle-class audiences.

Marie Lloyd, an icon of her day.

STRAINED

RELATIONS

Songs of Family Tensions

Unsurprisingly at a time of large families, small living quarters and economic worries, the working-class Victorian or Edwardian family home could be as much a place of tension as sanctuary. Father was often to blame. Titles like 'A Thing He Had Never Done Before', 'Following In Father's Footsteps' and the unambiguous 'We All Go To Work But Father' tell their own stories. The song 'Have You Paid The Rent?' despite a certain surreal quality enshrines a real enough question that must have been the cause of misery in many families. 'Half-Past Nine' has a new bride anxious to clear the house of obtrusive family so she and her new husband can go to bed, while the dependably unsubtle Harry Lauder takes to wearing a kilt so his wife cannot go through his trouser pockets when he is asleep.

A THING HE HAD NEVER DONE BEFORE *Sung by George Robey.*

Words and Music by C.W. Murphy. Arranged by Alfred Lamont.
© Copyright: Ascherberg, Hopwood and Crew, Ltd.
All Rights Reserved. International Copyright Secured.

Allegro moderato

The wind it blowed, the snow it snowed, the light-ning it did light, The rain came down as us - u - al, and, breth - ren, well it might; For had not darl - ing pa - pa come home so - ber that same night, A thing he had nev-er done be - fore! It took us all our time to hold the bull - dog Pat - sy Burke; And ma - ma tore her hair and start - ed rav - ing like a Turk, When pa - pa calm - ly told us that he'd been and done some work, A thing he had nev - er done be - fore!

Chorus

Verse 1

The wind it blowed, the snow it snowed, the lightning it did light
The rain came down as usual, and, brethren, well it might;
For had not darling papa come home sober that same night,
A thing he had never done before!
It took us all our time to hold the bulldog Patsy Burke;
And mama tore her hair and started raving like a Turk,
When papa calmly told that he'd been and done some work,
A thing he had never done before!

Chorus

'Twas a thing he had never done before,
Though he'd often been to prison to be sure;
It killed our sister Ruth,
When he went and spoke the truth,
A thing he had never done before. ▶

Verse 2

That very same papa was overjoyed last Sunday morn,
He'd never been so jolly since the day that I was born,
For he got his only pair of trousers out of pawn,
A thing he had never done before!
When mama saw that papa was a-treading virtue's path,
She said, Salvation Army-like, "Oh! What a soul he harth!"
She sold the clock for fourpence and then went and had a bath,
A thing she had never done before!

Chorus

'Twas a thing she had never done before,
Not even in the good old days of yore,
She thought she'd like a treat,
So she took on water neat,
A thing she had never done before!

Verse 3

When mama came home from the baths the old home went amiss;
Pa didn't recognize her so he shouted, "Who is this?"
He chuckled her underneath the chin, and gave her a kiss,
A thing he had never done before!
"Ah! Harold don't you know me? 'Tis your loving wife", she cried,
But dear papa had fainted, then to cheer him up we tried,
And as soon as he recovered, he committed suicide—
A thing he had never done before!

Chorus

'Twas a thing he had never done before,
To hop the twig unto another shore,
He'd a haircut and a shave,
When he laid him in his grave,
A thing he had never done before.

George Robey—born George Edward Wade in 1865—was one of the most successful of all Music Hall performers and, unlike most of them, had a middle-class upbringing. After being educated in England and Germany, he was destined first for the University of Leipzig, and then, on his father's return to England, for Cambridge. However, in one of those reversals of fortune so characteristic of a certain type of Music Hall song, he had to leave Cambridge abruptly when his father got into financial difficulties. Out of necessity he started to train as an engineer in Birmingham, where he also worked briefly as a clerk in the city's tram department. A fan of the legitimate theatre, Robey—who would eventually appear in Shakespeare on the stage, in Olivier's filmed *Henry V* and as Sancho Panza in G. W. Pabst's *Don Quixote*—became a singer and a comic performer in the halls almost by accident. He had volunteered to help a theatrical hypnotist, and was so good he was at once employed as a professional 'volunteer'. The man who would become one of Music Hall's most famous performers had begun a new career on the stage. He made his Music Hall debut at the age of 21 at the Oxford Music Hall in London's Oxford Street. Although he began as a singer, Robey was more noted on the halls for his comic routines than his songs. In fact the song most closely associated with him, 'If You Were the Only Girl in the World', was not even a Music Hall song at all; he made it famous in revue during World War I. In his Music Hall act, Robey enjoyed playing with language in the tradition of the chairmen of the old halls where contrived circumlocution, having failed to achieve the desired result, was traditionally followed by a brusque translation, as in 'Kindly temper your hilarity with a modicum of reserve … Desist!' It was a device successfully adapted much later by British comedian Frankie Howerd.

'A Thing He Had Never Done Before' revolves around a single gag replayed in each verse. The reliably badly behaved father of the family suddenly starts doing things which are uncharacteristically honest, hygienic, sober, prudent, affectionate and so on.

The startling unexpectedness of each new benevolent act gives us the title and the chorus. For the macabre climax, in the end even father himself is shocked by his own benign behaviour and kills himself, a grim turn of events that at least stays consistent with the song's refrain; this too was a thing he had never done before.

FOLLOWING IN FATHER'S FOOTSTEPS

Sung by Vesta Tilley.

Words and Music by F.W. Rogers.

Tempo di Polka

To fol-low in your fa-ther's foot-steps is a mot-to for each boy, And fol-low-ing in Fa-ther's foot-steps is a thing I much en-joy. My mo-ther caught me out one eve-ning, up the West End on the spree; She said, "Where are you go-ing?" but I ans-wered, "Don't ask *me!*"

Chorus
I'm fol-low-ing in fa-ther's foot-steps, I'm fol-low-ing the dear old dad. He's just in front with a fine big gal, so I thought I'd have

one as well. I don't know where he's go - ing but when he

gets there I'll be glad! I'm fol - low - ing in fa - ther's

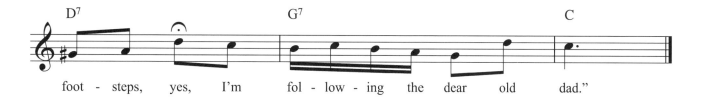

foot - steps, yes, I'm fol - low - ing the dear old dad."

Verse 1

**To follow in your father's footsteps is a
motto for each boy,
And following in father's footsteps is a
thing I much enjoy.
My mother caught me out one evening,
up the West End on the spree;
She said, "Where are you going?"
but I answered, "Don't ask *me*!"**

Chorus

**I'm following in father's footsteps,
I'm following the dear old dad.
He's just in front with a big fine gal,
so I thought I'd have one as well.
I don't know where he's going, but when he
gets there, I'll be glad!
I'm following in father's footsteps,
yes, I'm following the dear old dad.** ▶

Verse 2
Pa said that to the North of England he on bus'ness had to go,
To Charing Cross he went, and there he booked, I booked first class also.
I found myself that night in Paris, to the clergyman next door
I answered when he said,
"What are you in this gay place for?"

Chorus
To follow in your father's footsteps is a motto for each boy,
He's trav'ling now for his firm you see, in fancy goods it seems to me.
My mother caught me out one evening, up the West End on the spree;
She said, "Where are you going?" but I answered, "Don't ask *me!*"

Verse 3
At Margate with papa I toddled out to have a good old swim,
I didn't know the proper place to bathe, so I left it all to him.
I found myself amongst some ladies, and enjoyed it; so did pa!
Till ma yelled, "Percy, fie for shame!"
Said I, "It's alright ma!"

Chorus
To follow in your father's footsteps is a motto for each boy,
He's just out there with fair Miss Jupp to show me how to hold girls up.
I'm going to hold her next, ma, but when he drops her I'll be glad.
She said, "Where are you going?" but I answered, "Don't ask *me!*"

Verse 4
To dinner up in town last night I went, and pa went there as well,
How many "lemonades" we had— my word! I really couldn't tell.
At two a.m. pa started off for home, like this, and so did I!
Folks said, "Mind where you're going!" but I simply made reply—

Chorus
To follow in your father's footsteps is a motto for each boy,
He's wobbling on the front, you see, and 'pon my word he's worse than me.
My mother caught me out one evening, up the West End on the spree;
She said, "Where are you going?" but I answered, "Don't ask *me!*"

Vesta Tilley, born Matilda Alice Powles in 1864, was one of the Music Hall's leading male impersonators—the flipside of all those men in drag playing dames. Her stage name, acquired at the age of 11, combined the brand name of a famous smoker's match (Swan Vestas) with a diminutive of her real first name. Women playing men was generally a subtler business than the 'ugly sisters' approach of the men who mimicked women; the females nearly always aimed for an image of trim male elegance. It was a popular conceit on the halls and Tilley had many rivals, including Bessie Bonehill (who favoured patriotic songs), Bessie Wentworth, Hetty King, Ella Shields, May Henderson, and a host of pantomime principal boys: Florrie Forde, Ella Retford and Dorothy Ward and, memorably, Belle Bilton, a peer's wife who once, somewhat surreally, appeared at Drury Lane under her official name, Viscountess Dunlo.

The theatrical precedents for gender-swapping in this direction are numerous, notably in Shakespeare and Jacobean drama. Music Hall had its own ways of adding to irony of the male impersonation routine, not least through the choice of songs such as 'Following In Father's Footsteps', a title which surely resonates with Vesta Tiley's own childhood as the daughter of a comedy actor and sometimes theatre manager. She first appeared on stage at the age of three-and-a-half and at the age of six first dressed in male clothing to perform a skit where she portrayed a pocket-sized version of a famous contemporary opera singer. She would come to prefer doing male roles exclusively, saying that 'I felt that I could express myself better if I were dressed as a boy'. The polish and attention to detail of her performance became a byword and Vesta Tilley would be

associated with many successful songs including 'Algy, the Piccadilly Johnny', 'Jolly Good Luck to the Girl Who Loves a Soldier', 'The Army of Today's Alright' and, of course, 'Following in Father's Footsteps'.

This song had been composed at the turn of the century by E. W. Rogers, and it was a good example of the kind of number that Vesta Tilley did well, with its varied choruses and the way it lent itself to a smartly stepping male impersonator who depended on movement and stagecraft to reinforce the illusion that wasn't really an illusion. Since the *raison d'être* of this kind of act was usually the flair with which the impersonation was carried off, the song itself did not have to be a particularly strong or authentic one, and it has been argued that Vesta Tilley's songs were, in their way, not that far removed from the fantasy world of the *Lions comique*, that hedonistic realm of cost-free self-indulgence with few roots in reality.

'Following in Father's Footsteps' is no exception, with Father's drunken West End sprees, covert trips to Paris and shameless fondling of bathing girls right in front of his wife providing all-too-welcome parental examples for the 'son' to follow.

HALF-PAST NINE
(MY WEDDING DAY) Sung by Nellie Wallace.

Words and Music by Charles Collins.
© Copyright: Herman Darewski Music Publishing Co. Ltd.
All Rights Reserved. International Copyright Secured.

Verse 1

I'm longing for next Monday 'cos I'm going to tie the knot
With little Georgie Puddingy-Pie, a nice young man I've got.
And when the parson says the word that makes two into one,
I want you all to just come round and join us in the fun.

Chorus

For next Monday morning is my wedding day;
When the supper's over if the company wants to stay,
Me and me Georgie we shall resign,
We're going to blow the candles out at half-past nine!

Patter

Oh d-d-d-d-d-dear! I feel so excited today. No wonder girls, one doesn't get married very often, y'know. At least, I don't (*Very rapidly, chuckling*) Oh d-d-d-d-d-dear, what a life, what a life!

Verse 2

Now when we get back from the church, and the friends have all been in, And wished us joy and happiness in little drops of gin — (*Hiccup*) Oh dear! We want to both be on our own, I think its only fair. You may be sure that we don't want a lot of people there.

Chorus

Patter

Oh d-d-d-d-dear! Oh d-d-d-d-dear! I say, how do you like my dress, girls? Very becoming isn't it? I love the two-piece. Its so becoming to the slim figure. I love the slim figure. I love the long lining at the side here. Its one of Selfridge's, you know, one of Selfridge's. Specially from dear old Gordon. He's a darling boy, isn't he? This is my feather boa. D-d-d-d-dear! This weather plays havoc with your clothes. All out of curl. Pure down, too, pure down, all these feathers are, That's why it's so flat.

Verse 3

Now after we've had supper, I shall soon shut up the show. I will cut them all a slice of cake, and tell them all to go. And when I take the Vee of orange blossoms off my head — (*Chuckles*) I shall tell them all its time that we were fast asleep in bed.

Nellie Wallace's most notable ability as a performer was a capacity for portraying the gauche and awkward with warmth and humour that suggested affection rather than ridicule. Born Eleanor Jane Wallace in Glasgow in 1870, she had a voice that comes across very well in recordings, and a face that can be most kindly described as striking, especially in full make-up. The overall stage effect was usually completed with a curious get-up of ill-matching clothes and a tatty stole ('my little bit of vermin'). 'Half-Past Nine' (or 'My Wedding Day') is a rather basic song that revolves around the planned 9.30pm cut-off point for the impending wedding celebrations which is when the union is scheduled to be consummated — although of course the song's protracted avoidance of such an explicit phrase can be taken for granted.

So we are left with coy intimations about that consummation, such as 'We're going to blow the candles out' and 'We don't want a lot of people there'. This kind of euphemism was part of the course in the Music Hall song but Nellie Wallace animated this particular one with a lively delivery at which the printed lyrics can only hint. In her recording the verses are sung in short, sharp, staccato bursts into which are inserted giggles, chuckles and hiccups. When it comes to the chorus, however, she adopts a different technique. Instead of short bursts of song, she launches into a confident, joyous sweep of triumph as she regales us with the events planned for the ensuing Monday.

Some commentators saw Nellie Wallace as the natural heir to Jenny Hill, a much-admired serio-comic performer whose acting talents rounded out her music hall characters in a way that surpassed mere caricature. Here Nellie Wallace's patter is delivered in a very fast, tightly controlled voice and for once a reference to a well-known retailer of the day, Selfridge's, is not lost on a modern audience since the department store endures on London's Oxford Street. Less obvious is the playful reference to its founder, Harry Gordon Selfridge, whose name the singer drops as though he were a small local shop proprietor personally well known to her and her circle. The song's two-part title probably came about to distinguish it from an earlier quite different song called 'Half-Past Nine' which was the time of another consummation, this time between a married clerk and his lover tucked away in a discreet village.

Left: Nellie Wallace

HAVE YOU PAID THE RENT?

Sung by Harry Champion.

Words and Music by L. Silberman, Herbert Rule and Fred Holt.
© Copyright: Campbell Connelly & Co. Ltd.
All Rights Reserved. International Copyright Secured.

mo - ther says she's out, Have you paid the rent? Have you paid the rent?

Nev - er, nev - er, tell a lie. If you have - n't paid the rent.

One day you'll re - pent, And you won't go to heav - en when you die.

Verse 1

Everybody seems to be in trouble nowadays,
Trouble comes to all of us in many, many ways.
Everywhere you go, you'll hear a tale of woe,
The butcher wants to meet you when the baker wants his dough.
But there's one thing no one ever wants to pay,
This is why this is the latest saying of the day:

Chorus

Have you paid the rent?
Have you paid the rent?
Naughty, naughty, naughty, have you paid the rent?
Here's a wrinkle when the landlord is about,
Send the kiddies down to say that mother says she's out.
Have you paid the rent?
Have you paid the rent?
Never, never, tell a lie.
If you haven't paid the rent,
One day you'll repent,
And you won't go to heaven when you die. ▶

Verse 2
Charlie Brown was bathing in the sea and caught a cramp,
Stupid thing to do because the water was so damp.
Charlie shouted "Oh!", lobster caught his toe,
Charlie threw his arms up and he disappeared below.
Then the policeman came and at him had a look,
Said to Charlie Brown as he pulled out his little book:

Verse 3
Johnston spent the night out with no knocker on the door;
Got no door to hang the blessed knocker on no more.
No more roof remains, and though he still complains,
He has his dinner underneath the table when it rains.
And the neighbours' children make poor Johnston queer,
Shouting through the keyhole of the house that isn't there:

'Have You Paid the Rent?' is not a song to lift the spirits, adopting, as it does, a dreaded family phrase all too frequently heard in post-WWI Britain. It seems to reflect a change of spirit that touched the Music Hall just as it touched the entire country in the aftermath of the protracted conflict and during the hard times that followed. If, as seems most likely, the song was written after the war, then Champion seems to have recorded it at a time when his career was already beginning to decline. Not paying the rent would bring eviction, not comic social embarrassment, so it is not to be taken lightly, yet Harry Champion's 1922 recording of this song bowls along in a spirit if not exactly jolly at least brisk.

Possibly it is too brisk, as the singer fails to stress already feeble twin puns about foodstuffs ('the butcher wants to "meet" you and the baker wants his "dough"') and consequently the humour (for what it is worth) passes by unnoticed. This really is an odd song, far removed from Harry Champion's more usual pre-war fast-paced comic songs and celebrations of food. Even so, on the page at least, the piece has a slightly macabre and unsettling feel to it which must count for something. It starts as though it is going to celebrate a faddish catchphrase (have you paid the rent? 'is the latest saying of the day') which seems to align rent default with bobbed hair or the Charleston. But are we to assume that in the second verse Charlie

Brown has actually drowned and that even death does not remove the supreme obligation to have paid one's rent? Johnston's homecoming in the final verse is nothing less than surreal: there is no door knocker because there is no longer any door. There is no roof either and Johnston is obliged to eat his dinner underneath the table when it rains. The final image of children shouting through the keyhole of a door that does not exist to enquire if Johnston has paid his rent on a house that isn't there seems worthy of Magritte, Dali or Buñuel but somehow not of the man who before the war had extolled the simple and unambiguous virtues of boiled beef and carrots and a little bit of cucumber.

THAT'S THE REASON
NOO I WEAR A KILT
Sung by Harry Lauder.

Words and Music by Harry Lauder and A.B. Kendall.
© Copyright: 1906, Francis, Day & Hunter, Ltd.
All Rights Reserved. International Copyright Secured.

Moderato

A lot o' peo - ple say the kilt is not the thing to wear In

fat, they say the kilt is oot o' date; But I've got cer - tain rea - sons why I'm

wear - in' mine, and so I'll tell ye if ye on - ly care to wait. I

used to wear a pair o' breeks be - fore I took a wife, But

af - ter I'd been wed a week or three, I sold my troo - sers, bought this kilt, the

rea - son was be - cause I'll ex -plain it if you lis - ten noo tae me:

Ev - e - ry night I used to hing my troo - sers up on the back of the bed - room door. I rue the day I must have been a jay! I'll nev - er hing them up an - y more; For_ the wife she used to ram - ble through my pooch - es When I was fast a-sleep a-neath the quilt; In the morn - ing when I woke, I was al - ways sto - ney broke, That's the rea - son noo I wear a kilt.

Verse 1

A lot o' people say the kilt is not the thing to wear
In fact, they say the kilt is oot o' date;
But I've got certain reasons why I'm wearin' mine, and so
I'll tell ye if ye only care to wait.
I used to wear a pair o' breeks before I took a wife,
But after I'd been wed a week or three,
I sold my troosers, bought this kilt, the reason was because
I'll explain it if you listen noo tae me: ▶

Chorus

Every nicht I used to hing my troosers up
On the back o' the bedroom door.
I rue the day —
I must have been a jay!
I'll never hing them up any more;
For the wife she used to ramble through
my pooches
When I was fast asleep aneath the quilt;
In the morning when I woke,
I was always stoney broke —
That's the reason noo I wear a kilt.

Verse 2

I never would have found her oot,
but one nicht I cam' hame;
I was feelin' very queer aboot the head.
I soon was in the land o' dreams but
woke at three a.m.
And there she was a-standin' up in bed,
She said, "Hush, weesh! Be quiet!
There's burglars! dinna mak' a fuss!
I'm feelin' in your pooches for a gun."
I don't ken if she was or not, but all I
ken is this,
That there was naethin' in those
pooches when she'd done.

Verse 3

I'm not as strong's I used to be;
my blood is gettin' thin
And wouldna tak' an awfu' lot tae freeze.
The only thing I'm frightened for is
winter comin' on,
I'll feel it very cauld aboot the knees.
If I should take a freezin' fit one day
and kick the pail,
And join the Great Majority that's gone,
Then maybe I'll be sorry that I ever
took tae kilts,
And I'll wish I'd kept ma cosy troosers on.

London sometimes seems to have dominated Music Hall even though by its nature this style of entertainment was a nationwide phenomenon dependent on a circuit of local halls. Established early, London's halls had set the tone and encouraged informal networks of music publishers, performers and impresarios to flourish in the capital. Yet acts toured the provinces gratefully, one of the now often forgotten advantages being that the same routine appeared fresh in each new town or city—Liverpool audiences were unlikely to have seen the same performer do the same thing in Bristol or London a few nights earlier.

Like Variety that followed it, Music Hall depended on touring to extract maximum value from a routine. When television arrived in Britain after World War II, a single broadcast by an act, particularly a comedian, meant that everybody experienced it simultaneously and it could not easily be repeated either on TV or on stage. Radio, established earlier, had already started the process of erosion, but a visual medium gave away more of an artist's act.

When it came to touring an act, different cities or regions demanded different techniques, and the more quick-witted and adaptable performers were those who managed these modifications best. It was from the days of Music Hall that Glasgow's fearsome reputation as the graveyard of southern comedians was born. Yet Harry Lauder, who flaunted and exaggerated his Scottishness, was more than welcome south of the border and, eventually, all over the world. Ironically enough this uber-Scot originally took to the stage singing Irish songs, notably 'Calligan, Call Again'. That song tells of a pair of trousers for which Calligan the tailor is to be paid in instalments, but 'since I've had them trousers, well, my work has fallen short'—and thus, when Calligan calls for his money, he gets this response:
'Said I to Calligan,
"You'll have to call again."'

Lauder, who wrote many of his own songs, seems to have had something of a preoccupation with nether garments—witness the kilt song presented here. He was also instrumental in depicting Scots in a way that would today be considered unacceptably stereotypical. Thus 'That's the Reason Noo I Wear a Kilt' revolves around the spectacle of a man shivering with cold because he has adopted the key item of Scottish national dress simply in order to avoid his wife going through his trouser pockets at night. He wears the kilt not out of pride but out of domestic meanness. The song is written in the kind of phonetic language intended to suggest a dialect but that usually succeeds in only making even the best readers move their lips as they try to articulate the mangled words to see what they might mean.

Some of Lauder's other songs were variously romantic ('Roamin' in the Gloamin'', 'I Love a Lassie'), comic ('Stop Your Ticklin', Jock') or stirring ('Keep Right On to the End of the Road').

He was immensely popular and possessed considerable personal magnetism that seemed to outweigh his sometimes rudimentary and charmless songs. He was also very much a product of his age. Marie Lloyd, Gus Elen and Vesta Victoria are somehow not too hard to imagine as modern-day performers, but Harry Lauder, who in terms of fame eclipsed them all, now looks fixed in time, a talented man whose one-dimensional stage persona traded in sentimentality and national stereotype at a time when those qualities were welcomed, not questioned.

WE ALL GO TO WORK BUT FATHER Sung by J.C. Heffron.

Words and Music by Leslie Reed.
© Copyright: Francis, Day & Hunter, Ltd.
All Rights Reserved. International Copyright Secured.

Verse 1

Oh! we are a happy fam'ly and I mention it with pride
There's father, mother, me, and sister Fan.
It would be quite a model group that meets around our fireside
But father he is such a lazy man.
He has not done a day's work since the morning he was wed,
And that is five and twenty years ago.
No thought of work, in fact, has ever got into his head,
He's the laziest man I ever yet did know.

Patter

Lazy! Why, he's bone idle! Never does anything at all.
I wouldn't care if we set him a bad example, but we don't. In fact— ▶

Chorus
We all go to work but father
And he stays at home all day.
He sits by the fire with a quart of beer
And he smokes a ten-inch clay.
Mother works at the wash-tub,
So does my sister Fan;
I've met lazy men in my time, now and then,
but a champion is our old man.

Verse 2
He's in three sick societies, and that's the reason why
He vows to work he never will turn out.
He groans about his liver, then he'll hug his big toe and cry,
"Good gracious! Here's my old complaint, the gout!"
It seems at work he wasn't worth above a pound a week,
Though his was always "a very trying job".
And so each club in turn he patronises, so to speak,
By receiving just its merry thirty bob.

Patter
There's cheek for you! "Our heartless conduct",
"miss him when he's gone," and so on! But HE didn't stop
long. When we'd got the new place cosy—all the pictures hung,
carpets down and bedsteads fixed, a knocking came at the street
door, and there were two boys, with father stuck on his chair,
and two long poles shoved underneath, like Guy Fawkes. He'd
just waited till he thought all the work was done, and then he
gave the boys two pence to bring him home. I wouldn't care
if he did something sometimes; but he doesn't.

He was standing outside our door one day with his hands
in his pockets, when a gentleman asked him the way to the
post office. Just to show how lazy he is, he pointed with his foot
and said, "Up there". The gentleman said, "If you can show
me a lazier trick than that, I'll give you half-a-crown". Our
old man replied, "Alright, come and put it in my waistcoat
pocket". I expect when he's pegging out he'll want somebody else
to draw his last breath for him. So now you can believe me when I say:

Chorus

J.C. Heffron is best remembered for the lively novelty number 'Where Did You Get That Hat?' although 'We All Go To Work But Father' was apparently the more influential song, somehow becoming a medicine show favourite in the United States in 1905 where it was called 'Everybody Works But Father'. That Americanised version of a British song was even eventually performed by Groucho Marx in both English and German on a TV show while blues singer Jesse Fuller, famous for his recording of 'San Francisco Bay Blues' included it on a 1963 album *Brother Lowdown*.

Oddly the original Music Hall version written by Leslie Reed has very little tension or development — it simply keeps reiterating 'father's' impressive capacity for idleness. While every other family member works, he doesn't. We learned as much from the title and we learn little else since the put-upon family seems unable to mount any effective counter-attack to such dedicated indolence. Even when they all move house and leave father behind unsupported he follows them to their new home…but only after a decent interval because he fears work might have been expected from him had he shown up too soon. Comic exaggeration of his laziness rings a few diverting changes but does nothing to advance the story.

In no way a social commentary, the song nonetheless sadly illuminates one dispiriting tenet of family life in the world from which it sprang—that blood is thicker than water. It is clear that the demands made upon the family simply cannot be shrugged off, whatever the provocation. Father wins. The virtue that triumphs here is not that of the industrious worker but simply that of the status of *paterfamilias*. Family responsibility is portrayed as grim duty—a shackle that it seems could not be broken even when the jailer was as charmless as 'father'.

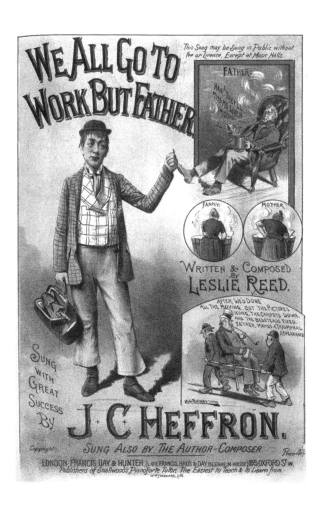

Pricking the BUBBLE

Songs of
Satire and Deflation

'**B**urlington Bertie From Bow' is a sustained exercise in deflating the image of the well-to-do *flâneur* immortalised in the original 'Burlington Bertie' song. It does this by turning him into an East End lad who apes the mannerisms of the West End socialites without actually having any money. Other songs in this section satirise everything from the hypocrisy of the courts through the incompetence of a fire brigade to the perceived pretentiousness of Shakespeare, several of whose creations are cut down to size by applying a no-nonsense Music Hall treatment. All are symptomatic of Music Hall's great love of seeing the high and mighty brought low. If the audience could not afford to hobnob with Champagne Charlie and Burlington Bertie, they could at least enjoy puncturing their pretension.

BURLINGTON BERTIE FROM BOW

Sung by Ella Shields.

Words and Music by William Hargreaves.
© Copyright 2013 Dorsey Brothers Music Limited.
All Rights Reserved. International Copyright Secured.

Moderato

I'm Bert, p'raps you've heard of me.

Bert, you've had word of me. Plod-ding a-long,____

health-y and strong,____ liv-ing on plates of fresh air.

I dress up in fa-shion, and when I am

feel-ing de-pressed I shave from my cuff all the whis-kers and

fluff, stick my hat on and tod-dle up West. I'm

Chorus

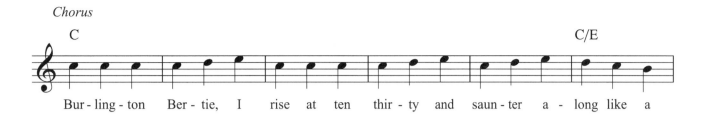

Bur - ling - ton Ber - tie, I rise at ten thir - ty and saun - ter a - long like a

toff. I walk down the Strand with my gloves on my hand, then I

walk down a - gain with them off. I'm all airs and gra - ces, cor - rect ea - sy

pa - ces, so long with - out food I've for - got where my face is. I'm Bert,

Bert, I have - n't a shirt, but my peo - ple are well off you know.

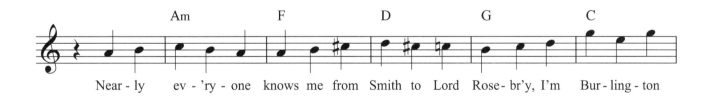

Near - ly ev - 'ry - one knows me from Smith to Lord Rose - br'y, I'm Bur - ling - ton

Ber - tie from Bow.

Verse 1

I'm Bert, p'raps you've heard of me.
Bert, you've had word of me.
Plodding along, healthy and strong,
Living on plates of fresh air.
I dress up in fashion,
And when I'm feeling depressed,
I shave from my cuff all the whiskers and fluff,
Stick on my hat and toddle up West.

Chorus

I'm Burlington Bertie,
I rise at ten thirty
And saunter along like a toff.
I walk down the Strand
With my gloves on my hand,
Then I walk down again with them off.
I'm all airs and graces
Correct easy paces,
So long without food
I've forgot where my face is.
I'm Bert, Bert, I haven't a shirt,
But my people are well off you know.
Nearly ev'ry-one knows me
From Smith to Lor Rose-br'y,
I'm Burlington Bertie from Bow.

Verse 2

I stroll with Lord Hurlington, roll in The Burlington,
Call for Champagne, walk out again,
Come back and borrow the ink.
I live most expensive
Like Tom Lipton, I'm in the swim.
He's got so much 'oof' that he sleeps on the roof,
And I live in the room over him.

Chorus 2

I'm Burlington Bertie,
I rise at ten thirty
And saunter along Temple Bar.
And round there I skip,
I keep shouting "Pip, Pip"
And the darn'd fools think I'm in my car.

At Rothchilds I swank it,
My body I plank it
On his front doorstep
With 'The Mail' for a blanket.
I'm Bert, Bert, and Rothchild was hurt.
He said, "You can't sleep there."
I said, "Oh!"
He said "I'm Rothchild sonny."
I said, "That's damn'd funny,
I'm Burlington Bertie from Bow."

Verse 3
My pose, though ironical, shows
That my monocle holds up my face,
Keeps it in place,
Stops it from slipping away.
Cigars, I smoke thousands,
I usually deal in The Strand.
But you've got to take care
When you're getting them there,
Or some idiot might stand on your hand.

Chorus 3
I'm Burlington Bertie,
I rise at ten thirty,
And Buckingham Palace I view.
I stand in the yard
While they're changing the guard
And the Queen shouts across "Toodle oo!"
The Prince of Wales brother
Along with some other
Slaps me on the back and say,
"Come and see Mother."
But I'm Bert, Bert,
And Royalty's hurt,
When they ask me to dine I say "No."
I've just had a banana
With Lady Diana.
I'm Burlington Bertie from Bow.

This famous Music Hall song benefits from a few background notes, not least for those unfamiliar with the districts of London and their relative prosperity back in the early 1900s. 'Burlington Bertie From Bow' was an 'answer' song, that is to say it was a response to an earlier one. The earlier one in this case was 'Burlington Bertie'; it dated from 1900 and was sung by Vesta Tilley in her usual male dress stage outfit. That Burlington Bertie bore a close resemblance to George Leybourne's 'Champagne Charlie' in that both were louche toffs whose lives might trigger jealousy but could not be said to have anything much in common with most Music Hall audiences.

William Hargreaves' deflationary 1915 response 'Burlington Bertie From Bow' was to eclipse the original almost completely. His song was performed by his wife Ella Shields, another male impersonator act. Shields hailed from Baltimore, Maryland, but was lured to Britain which she soon made her permanent home. The song casts a lad from Bow in East London—then a very poor area—as a self-styled aristocrat aping the mannerisms and dress of the gentry while strolling about the more wealthy districts of London without a penny to his name. 'I'm Burlington Bertie I rise at ten thirty and saunter along like a toff / I walk down The Strand with my gloves on my hand / Then I walk down again with them off.'

Hargreaves sustains the conceit nicely through a very long lyric. 'Cigars, cigars, I smoke thousands / I usually deal in The Strand / But you've got to take care when you're getting them there / Or some idiot might step on your hand'.

Here was proof if it were needed that a song which pricked the bubble of wealthy affectation would be far more popular in the halls than one which, a few years earlier, had simply told of the good life enjoyed by the idle rich. 'Burlington Bertie From Bow' became 'the' Burlington Bertie song and many heard it without even being aware of the original it was guying. Its central conceit—a woman dressed as a man pretends to be wealthy while showing signs of poverty—was revisited in the 1948 film *Easter Parade* where Judy Garland in male drag joins Fred Astaire to perform Irving Berlin's 'We're A Couple Of Swells'. In 1968 Julie Andrews sang

Burlington Bertie From Bow' in the film *Star!* and it is thought that she based her gender-bending role in *Victor/Victoria* partly on Shields with whom she had worked in a Royal Variety Show when she was very young.

Ella Shields' career stalled as did those of so many other Music Hall acts during the 1930s; at one point she returned to the USA and worked as an assistant in Macy's department store. Burlington Bertie had dogged her footsteps and would do so again. A nostalgic revival of Music Hall acts in the 1940s and early 1950s saw her back in Britain reprising her old songs until, like Marie Lloyd, she too collapsed on stage and died soon afterwards.

Ella Shields in the Burlington Bertie guise that made her famous. For her final performance of the song at the age of 72 she changed the first line to the past tense:
'I was Burlington Bertie From Bow...'
She collapsed on stage after singing it and died three days later.

HIS LORDSHIP WINKED AT THE COUNSEL

Sung by Harry Rickards.

Words by George Dance. Music by Peter Conroy.

Allegretto

The Judge took his seat in the court-house one day, A nice Breach of Prom-ise to hear,_____ The Plain-tiff stepped up with a veil round her face, A love-ly and blush-ing young dear._____ She looked at the Ju-ry a sly lov-ing glance, she smiled at the Coun-sel be-low,_____ Then turn-ing her soft pret-ty eyes to the Judge, She ten-der-ly mur-mured,"Hei ho!"_____

Chorus

His Lord-ship winked at the Coun-sel, The Coun-sel winked at the Clerk;_____ The Ju-ry passed a wink a-long and mur-mured,"Here's a lark!"_____ The Ush-er winked at the Bob-by, the Bob-by left his seat,_____ And turn-ing to the win-dow winked At some-bo-dy out in the street._____

Verse 1

The Judge took his seat in the
court-house one Day,
A nice Breach of Promise to hear,
The Plaintiff stepped up with a veil
round her Face,
A lovely and blushing young dear.
She looked at the Jury a sly loving glance,
She smiled at the council below,
Then turning her soft pretty eyes to the Judge,
She tenderly murmured, "Heigh-ho".

Chorus

His Lordship winked at the Counsel,
The Counsel winked at the Clerk;
The Jury passed a wink along
And murmured, "Here's a lark!"
The Usher winked at the Bobby,
The Bobby left his seat,
And turning to the window winked
At somebody out in the street.

Verse 2

"Pray tell us the facts of your case",
the Judge said,
"Your wrongs we are anxious to hear".
"I'll try, my good Lord," the sweet
maiden replied,
"My poor heart is broken, I fear.
The monster who wooed me,
declared on his Oath,
He'd make me his bride by-and-by,
He took me long walks in the moonlight alone
And kissed me when no one was nigh."

Chorus

His Lordship grinned at the Counsel,
The Counsel grinned at the Clerk;
The Jury passed a grin along
And murmured, "Here's a lark!"
The Usher grinned at the Bobby,
The Bobby left his seat,
And turning to the window grinned
At somebody out in the street.

Verse 3

The Judge took a pinch of his
pungent rappee,
And dignity spread o'er his face.
"You really must name him, my sweet
pretty maid,
Or we can't proceed with the case."
The maiden then snatched the thick
veil from her cheeks,
And smiled like a mischievous elf;
Then turning around to the Judge
cried, "My Lord,
The false-hearted man is yourself". ▶

Chorus

His Lordship blushed at the Counsel,
The Counsel blushed at the Clerk;
The Jury passed a blush along
And murmured, "Here's a lark!"
The Usher blushed at the Bobby,
The Bobby left his seat,
And turning to the window blushed
At somebody out in the street.

Verse 4

The Judge viewed the charms of the girl
he once loved
And longed her lips once more to press,
"Oh sweet pretty maid will you marry
me now?"
She blushingly answered him, "Yes."
They sent for a Parson, they sent
for a clerk,
And ere one short hour had sped,
They threw all the fusty law
papers aside,
And each held a Prayer Book instead.

Chorus

His Lordship tickled the Counsel.
The Counsel tickled the Clerk;
The Jury passed the tickle along
And murmured, "Here's a lark!"
The Usher tickled the Bobby,
The Bobby left his seat,
And turning to the window tickled
At somebody out in the street.

There are many songs that feature comical policemen but rather less that seek to find comedy or romance inside the courtroom. The law, it has been said, does not have a sense of humour. Harry Rickards' song 'His Lordship Winked At The Counsel' took a successful shot at it however, choosing subject matter rather similar to the plot of Gilbert and Sullivan's comic opera *Trial by Jury*. Rickards' number tells a simpler story with a single twist in the tail that contrasts with *Trial By Jury*'s more complex convolutions; even so, the payoff is the same. George Dance wrote the words, Peter Conroy composed the music and the result became one of Harry Rickards' two best-known songs.

The other was 'Knocked 'Em In The Old Kent Road' which also attracted many other artists, perhaps the least plausible being by Marlene Dietrich who had to wrestle with south London-accented lines like '"Wotcher!" all the neighbours cried / Oo yer gonna meet, Bill / 'Ave yer bought the street, Bill?'

'His Lordship Winked At The Counsel' revisits a favourite theme of Victorian songwriters, the dual standards that applied to the working class and the upper classes. The judge is imperious and patronising until it is revealed that, on this occasion, he is in no position to be either.

Croydon-born Harry Rickards had his own unpleasant experience in the English law courts, being declared bankrupt. Even so his real successes came in business rather than through performing (even 'Knocked 'Em In The Old Kent Road' was a bigger success for Albert Chevalier than for him). Following his experience in the courts, he responded by making a new life in Australia, becoming a highly successful impresario there. He also became the owner of Sydney's Garrick Theatre, rechristening it the *Tivoli* and making it the hub of the Tivoli Circuit. Every year he visited England and over a period of time he hired for the Australian circuit many top variety and vaudeville artists that included Harry Houdini and Marie Lloyd.

I LIVE IN TRAFALGAR SQUARE

Sung by Morny Cash.

Words and Music by C.W. Murphy.
© Copyright: 1902, Francis, Day & Hunter, Ltd.
All Rights Reserved. International Copyright Secured.

Verse 1

Today I've been busy removing
And I'm all of a fidgety-fidge;
My last digs were on the Embankment,
The third seat from Waterloo Bridge!
But the cooking and, Oh! The
attendance,
Didn't happen to suit me so well,
So I ordered my man to pack up, and
Look out for another hotel.
He did, and the new place is
"extra," I vow!
Just wait till I tell you where I'm
staying now:

Chorus

I live in Trafalgar Square
With four lions to guard me.
Fountains and statues all over the place,
And the "Metropole" staring me
right in the Face!
I'll own it's a trifle draughty,
But I look at it this way you see,
If its good enough for Nelson,
It's quite good enough for me!

Verse 2

The beds ain't so soft as the might be,
Still the temp'rature's never too high!
And it's nice to see swells who are passing,
Look on you with envious eye.
And when you wake in the morning
To have a good walk for your breakfast,
And the same for your dinner and tea!
There's many a swell up in Park Lane tonight
Who'd be glad if he only had my
appetite.

Verse 3

When I think of those unlucky bounders,
The Morgans and Clarence de Clares,
Who are forced to put up at the "Cecil,"
My tenderest sympathy's theirs!
And to show I'm not selfish or greedy,
I just tell each aristocrat,
That I don't mind exchanging apartments,
Now, I can't say fairer than that!
But the soft-headed sillies wont
hear what I say,
They still go on suff'ring,
while I'm all O.K.

Morny Cash, known as the Lancashire Lad, seems to be a rather obscure performer who probably made his debut at the City Varieties Music Hall in Leeds. He certainly appeared on the bill there in 1912 and his song 'I Live In Trafalgar Square' was written in 1902 by Clarence Wainwright Murphy, a truly prolific British composer of music hall and musical theatre tunes of which the best known is probably 'Has Anybody Here Seen Kelly?'

Some critical assessments of 'I Live In Trafalgar Square' have sought to invest it with an exclusively satirical agenda. The truth is probably that the tramp's inflated description of the joys of sleeping rough are primarily intended to entertain by the familiar process of inverting values and stressing incongruities, and only on a secondary level can be seen as satire on the shallowness and false importance of the life lived by the swells who pass by. Similar examples litter the popular American songbooks, from Harry MacLintock's 'Hallelujah, I'm A Bum' through Irving Berlin's 'We're A Couple Of Swells' to Roger Miller's 'King Of The Road'. To be sure there is a touch of irony in the inversions, but that is what raises a smile: the temperature is never too high in this *al fresco* existence and there are surely many living in the luxury of Park Lane who would be glad of the singer's appetite. Isolated, these could be seen as sarcastic observations, but in context they are a consistently logical part of the song's topsy-turvy world. The chorus works well and the first two lines offer an amusing interpretation of sleeping out in the famous square with the four Landseer lions 'guarding' the sleeping tramp. The last couplet too is amusing if a touch defensive: 'If it's good enough for Nelson / It's good enough for me!'

ONE OF THE DEATHLESS ARMY

Sung by Little Tich.

Words by T. W. Thurban. Music by Gilbert Wells, Will Terry and V.R. Gill.
© Copyright: Francis, Day & Hunter, Ltd.
All Rights Reserved. International Copyright Secured.

Allegretto

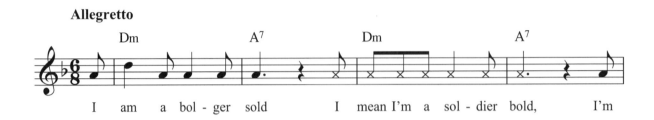

I am a bol - ger sold I mean I'm a sol - dier bold, I'm

not so young as I used to be be - fore I got so old. I

am a reg - u - lar toff I am, I am, I say I am; But you

can't tell what's in - side the jar by the la - bel on the jam.

Chorus

For I'm_____ a sol - dier, a Ter - ri - tor - i - al. The

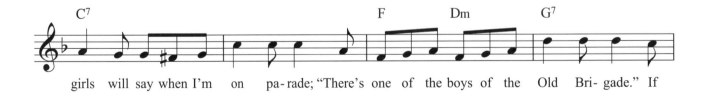

girls will say when I'm on pa - rade; "There's one of the boys of the Old Bri- gade." If

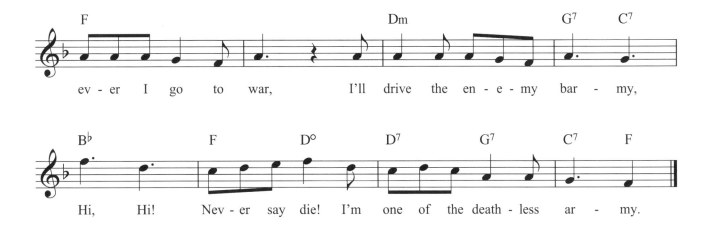

ev - er   I   go   to   war,   I'll   drive   the   en - e - my   bar - my,

Hi,   Hi!   Nev - er   say   die!   I'm   one   of   the   death - less   ar - my.

Verse 1

I am a bolger sold—I mean I'm a soldier bold,
I'm not so young as I used to be before I got so old.
I am a regular toff I am, I am, I say I am;
But you can't tell what's inside the jar by the label on the jam.

Chorus

For I'm a soldier, a Territorial.
The girls will say when I'm on parade
"There's one of the boys of the Old Brigade."
If ever I go to war, I'll drive the enemy barmy,
Hi, Hi! Never say die!
I'm one of the deathless army.

Patter

(*to pathetic music*): Would you like me to tell you the
story, sir, of the horribleness of war? Well, it was half-past
six in the morning, sir, when the clock struck five-to-four-
there was something went wrong with the works, sir, but the
enemy wanted a fight. Why, they lay with our right on their left,
sir, and we lay with our left on their right. And I wanted a
Turkish Bath, sir, but the colonel said, "there is
no hope". For the drummer boy is drunk all the water and the
bugler's swallowed the soap. I lay down and shrieked in my
anguish, but the colonel said, "Lad, never mind, why, you ▶

Harry Relph, aka Little Tich,
adopting his classic stance.

haven't got on any trousers!" Huh! So I went in and pulled down the blind. Then the bugler tootled his tooter, and I knew that the foeman was nigh, so I rushed out to buy some tobacco, when a cannon ball flopped in my eye. You know, I could scarcely see for a moment and I thought it was very unkind. Then the colonel's wife dropped in to see me and said, "Er, shall we, er, pull down the blind?" Then the enemy clustered around us, and the colonel went clean off his chump. And the horses drew horse and stampeded, and the camels had all got the hump. Well I was having a whiskey and soda, sir, when a shot struck me, er, somewhere behind. As I could not pull it out in the street, sir, I went in and pulled down the blind. And the shells lay around me in thousands, and still they continued to drop. So I payed for the dozen I'd eaten and walked out of the oyster shop. And the shots they were buzzing around me, and one nearly blew off my head. There were cannons to right of me, cannons to left of me—so what did I do? Went in off the red.

Chorus

Little Tich was the stage name of Harry Relph, born in 1867 and destined to be short of stature (he never exceeded four feet six inches [1.37 m] in height) as well as being further distinguished by having five fingers and a thumb on each hand and six toes on each foot. His stage name derived from a notorious 19th-century legal case in which the very overweight Arthur Orton falsely claimed to be Sir Roger Tichborne, the missing heir to the Tichborne Baronetcy. The sudden celebrity of the Tichborne name plus the contrast between very big Arthur Orton and very small Harry Relph suggested the name Little Tich. Henceforth the word 'Tich' or 'Titch' was used to suggest something miniature, so making Harry Relph a contributor to the English language. He was a comic actor who sang, originating a selection of 'types' such as the Gendarme, the Spanish Señora and the Tax Collector. These characters allowed him to present his act on the continental mainland as well as in Britain. For his performances at the Folies Bergère he was made an officer of the French Academy. He also affected a giant pair of 28-inch slap shoes in which he performed his famous Big Boot dance which was recorded in a solitary piece of film for the Phono-Cinéma-Théâtre in 1900, and was described by Jacques Tati as the basis 'for everything that has been realised in comedy on the screen'.

What is presented here is a shortened version of one of his acts taken from a pre-WWI recording where the volunteer soldier is the butt of the joke. Sketchy though it is, it gives some idea of a particularly interesting kind of music hall entertainment where the verse and chorus serve as parentheses to the long patter which forms the main substance of the act. This patter was absurdist but delivered in a robust declamatory style for maximum incongruity. It burlesques the then-new Territorial Army (a volunteer force founded in Britain in 1908) in which Little Tich seemed to find a rich vein of comedy— witness too his 'Since Poor Father Joined the Territorials' spoofing the earnestness of the part-time warrior:

Since poor father joined the Territorials
Ours is a happy little home!
He wakes us up in the middle of the night
And says we all must be prepared to fight!
He puts poor mother in the dustbin to stand on sentry-guard;
And me and brother Bert,
In his little flannel shirt,
He keeps drilling in the old back yard!

The sung part of 'The Deathless Army' was presented straight, as if it were a natural and logical account, the absurdity not being played up in the telling. Only the most subtle exaggerations would have suggested to the contemporary listener a satire on the dramatic monologue of the period. This changes when the patter strikes as confiding tone and Little Tich adopts his own stage persona, not that of the supposed singer of the song. This rather precise playing of parts was also reflected in Little Titch's careful separation of his stage and real-life selves. He was shy and did not like to joke or seek approval privately. All he wanted was recognition as an artist. Little Tich took his comedy seriously.

THE PENNY WHISTLER *Sung by Paul Mill.*

Words by Paul Mill. Music by George D. Fox.
© Copyright: Francis, Day & Hunter, Ltd.
All Rights Reserved. International Copyright Secured.

Tempo Gavotte, moderato

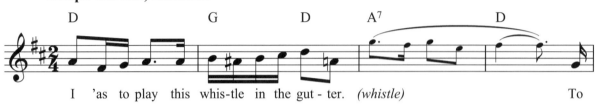

I 'as to play this whis-tle in the gut - ter. *(whistle)* To

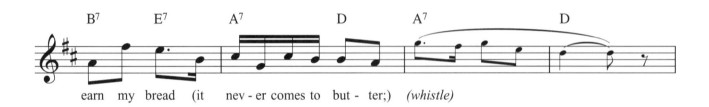

earn my bread (it nev - er comes to but - ter;) *(whistle)*

All day long I wan-ders 'round the 'ous - es though I blow my best the game don't pay; There's

'oles in my coat and patch-es on my *(whistle)*

Refrain

(whistle)

I 'as to play this whistle in the gutter *(Whistle)*
To earn my bread (it never comes to butter); *(Whistle)*
All day long I wanders round the 'ouses,
Though I blow my best the game don't pay;
There's 'oles in my coat and patches on my—*(Whistle)*.

I, as a boy, got little education, *(Whistle)*
Boys now learn things far above their station; *(Whistle)*
With French and stuff the kids they fairly flummox;
The School Board really ought to try, instead
Of cramming their 'eads, to fill their little—*(Whistle)*

Ladies for dress 'ave always 'ad a passion—*(Whistle)*
And though they starve, they will be in the fashion; *(Whistle)*
About their togs we're always 'aving tussles,
Things called "bloomers" is the latest craze,
But one thing I've noticed, they've turned up wearing—
(Whistle)

What is the good of these 'ere politicians; *(Whistle)*
They don't help us talented musicians! *(Whistle)*
When they want yer votes yer think they're tryers,
For then they say they'll give us this and that,
But it never comes off—No! They're a lot of—*(Whistle)*

I 'as a long, strong struggle for my "vittles", *(Whistle)*
For I don't come across the beer and skittles. *(Whistle)*
But in one thing we are on a level;
Parsons tell us we are all born bad
And if doesn't alter, we're going to the—*(Whistle)*.

'The Penny Whistler' is on the surface a simple novelty song built around the idea of a running commentary on issues of the day as seen by what we might call a penniless whistler. Yet afflicted by poverty as he is, this feisty musical observer has prickly theories on education, fashion, politics and religion. In each verse the terminal word is omitted and replaced by piped note. The context and expected rhyme suggest what the word would have been. If this had been Max Miller, the unarticulated missing word would have been suggestive or obscene but here it is nothing more than missing, the joke lying in the simple substitution of musical note for guessable word. Its singer, Paul Mill, presumably played the penny whistle too, a suitably cheeky, plaintive and inexpensive instrument for this musical broadside from the bottom of society. This was neither the first nor the last song to insert a musical quotation from 'Home, Sweet Home', the famously mawkish song by Sir Henry Bishop and John Howard Payne. It was a cliché that not only provided muscial shorthand for 'home' but also brought with it the cloyingly sentimental tone of that song. Does our penny whistler have a home? It seems unlikely since he can hardly afford food. He might have added an acerbic verse to his song about the songwriters of that hymn to the home of whom the normally even-tempered critic Maurice Willson Disher once observed waspishly 'the names associated with "Home, Sweet Home" (Henry Bishop and John Howard Payne), are at best those of incorrigible wanderers and at the worst of a downright home wrecker'. Oddly the effect of Paul Mill's song is, if not jolly, at least far from morbid. Its sense of streetwise sarcasm, as it dishes out advice to those more fortunately placed, suggests an undefeated spirit. What is striking is not the poverty itself but the singer's independence in spite of it.

'The Penny Whistler' is another example of the Music Hall's occasional attempts to marry pathos, comedy and social criticism. It is a minor example but one which in its modest way succeeds.

THE FIRE WAS BURNING HOT Sung by T.E. Dunville.

Words and Music by T.W. Connor.
© Copyright: Bowerman & Co.
All Rights Reserved. International Copyright Secured.

Verse 1
Our gallant men were fast asleep
Awaiting duty's call,
When someone brought the fearful news
That mesmerised us all.
A chimney pot was smoking
Only ten miles further on,
And if we didn't hurry up,
The beer would all be gone.

Patter
I forgot to ask where the fire was,
but wrote a letter at once to the turncock, and
sent a man round to the wheelwright's to see
when the engine would be finished. As it
happened, the horses were out doing a funeral
job. When they came home, I had to take
'em to the farriers, and after that we made a
start. When we got there we found the fire
was on the fourth storey, and our ladder
only reached to the second. So we had to wait
till the fire got down, or call again to-morrow.
Captain gave us three weeks to consider and
In the meantime—

Chorus
The first was burning hot,
And the water was perishing cold;
Our gallant lads all parched and dry,
Watching from the pub close by;
And when the fire was out,
Like heroes they behaved,
And every soul in that empty house
That didn't get burnt got saved! ▶

We searched in all the jewellers' shops,
But no plug could we find;
Our Captain shouted, "Cheer up, boys,
We've left the hose behind!"
Then up the gutter spout he rushed,
His whiskers tied in knots,
And rubbed some hokey-pokey on
To cool the chimney pots.

Patter
Wonderful man our Captain—got
three medals and a dog-bite.
Made a patent fire-escape, all out of his
own head. Swears in fourteen
languages. He only left us once while
he went to have his boots cleaned. Then
sombody went and put hot water
on the fire, which, of course, made it ten
times worse.
and in the meantime—

Chorus

Verse 3
At last we got the fire alight,
And swallowed all the smoke,
We couldn't reach the windows, so
We smashed up all the coke;
We cheered ourselves—
with bated breath,
We knew not what about,
And never left till all the pubs
Were fairly gutted out

Patter
Then came the welcome order—
single men go home, married
men stop out for a change.
I was one of 'em,
and it was hot work—
stopping out all night, but
duty's duty, whether it is or not,
and besides—

Chorus

Verse 4
We drew our faithful choppers out
And put 'em back again,
And thanked out lucky stars we'd all
Got water on the brain;
Our fireproof whiskers turned to (h)air
As the roof turned inside out;
We shut out eyes,
and looked and looked—
Like idiots, no doubt.

Chorus

T.W. Connor wrote 'The Fire Was Burning Hot' which, in the main, manages to be very funny in an absurdist sort of way. Its singer, T. E. Dunville, had a reputation for nonsense songs that had a strand of social realism in them, and he excelled at delivering their more punchy comic lines with accomplishment. Peter Davison points out that a T. E. Dunville song often brought to mind the staccato telegrammatic speech patterns of Dickens' Alfred Jingle in *The Pickwick Papers*. Another Dunville song, 'Little Billie Bates', which concerns a fatal skating accident, summarises the coroner's verdict with:

Little boy—
Pair of skates—
Hole in ice—
Heaven's gates.

'The Fire Was Burning Hot' is not quite as spare as that but it certainly crams a lot of words into lyrics and patter, with non-sequiturs vying with absurdities to paint a word-picture of the sort of fire brigade unlikely to reassure anyone trapped in a burning building. 'Our gallant men were fast asleep / Awaiting duty's call' is the firefighter's discouraging start. Not exactly a fast-response unit, this brigade reacts to news of a fire by sending a man round to the wheelwright to see when the fire engine will be finished.

The standard of the comedy falls off later on in the song although the occasional burst of misplaced self-congratulation in the face of unremitting incompetence does raise a smile. ('Wonderful man our captain…swears in fourteen languages'.) T. E. Dunville, real name Thomas Edward Wallen, came from Coventry and was billed as an 'eccentric comedian' who blended comic physical contortions with his verbal ones. P. G. Wodehouse referenced him in his book *The Swoop!* which suggests some degree of general fame even though Dunville suffered from a career that only took off after World War I when the halls were already starting to decline. Gradually his act became less popular and after an appearance at the Grand, Clapham, South London on 20 March 1924 at the age of 57, he disappeared, and his body was found in the Thames near Reading two days later.

THE MUSIC HALL SHAKESPEARE Sung by Emil Clare.

Written by Worton David. Music by Harry Fragson.
© Copyright: Francis, Day & Hunter, Ltd.
All Rights Reserved. International Copyright Secured.

tree._____ If I die, where shall I go? Ev - en John Bull

does - n't know, To be or_____ not__ to be._____

2nd Chorus

Oh, Oh, An - to - ni - o, you'll have to

pay._____ Through you are stone - y - -

- o, I'll have my own - i - o.

I'll have my pound of flesh cut from

your heart._____ And I'll hawk it round at four-pence a

pound in my ice cream cart._____

3rd Chorus

Hal - lo, Hal - lo, Hal - lo,_____ It's a dif - fe - rent wife a - gain._____ With

dif - fe - rent eyes, dif - fe - rent nose, Dif - fe - rent hair, dif - fe - rent toes Hal -

- lo, Hal - lo, Hal - lo,_____ To me it's fair - ly plain,_____ He's

tick - led the chin of Anne Bo - lyne, It's a dif - fe - rent wife a - gain._____

169

Verse 1
Shakespeare wrote a lot plays,
Tragedies of olden days,
Wrote 'em in a manner far from gay.
Often it occurs to me,
How much brighter they would be
Written in a music-hally way.
Take "To be or not to be,"
Hamlet's famed soliloquy,
Nowadays the point it seems to miss.
But revise the tune a bit,
Put a catchy tune to it,
And Hamlet's speech would
turn out more
Like this:

Chorus 1
(To: 'Let's All Go Down the Strand'—
Charles Whittle)
To be or not to be?
To be or not to be?
If I live, Ophelia I must wed,
If I die I shall be a long time dead.
To be or not to be?
I'm fairly up a tree.
If I die, where shall I go?
Even John Bull doesn't know,
To be or not to be?

Verse 2
Take another Shakespeare play,
Fairly brutal I'm afraid,
In which Shylock plays the leading part.
He's the Jew, of course you know,
Who from young Antonio
Claims a pound of flesh cut from the heart.
Anger flashing from his eyes—
"Curse the Christian dog," he cries,
"I will have my pound of flesh this day."

How much nicer it would seem,
If instead of tragedy
Shylock to Antonio did say:

Chorus 2
(To: 'Oh, Oh Antonio'—Florrie Forde)
Oh, Oh, Antonio, you'll have to pay.
Though you are a stony-o,
I'll have my own-io.
I'll have my pound of flesh cut
from your heart
And I'll hawk it round at fourpence a pound
On my ice-cream cart.

Verse 3
Next a character I'll quote
From a play that Shakespeare wrote,
King Henry the Eighth—a wicked lot.
Half-a-dozen wives had he,
When with one he couldn't agree.
He divorced her and a fresh one got.
Till at last in righteous wrath,
Wolsey cried out, "By my troth,
This man's a libertine."
Off comes his head!
But his majesty explains,
On the music halls today,
Wolsey would have simply winked and said:

Chorus 3
(To: 'It's a Different Girl Again'—Whit Cunliffe)
Hallo, Hallo, Hallo,
It's a different wife again
With different eyes, different nose,
Different hair, different toes!
Hall, Hallo, Hallo,
To me it's fairly plain,
He's ticked the chin of Anne Boleyn,
It's a different wife again.

In the days of Music Hall, popular parody of Shakespeare was nothing new but it was still perhaps seen as a piece of daringly iconoclastic mischief at a time when some of the more serious-minded comics might very well wish to play Hamlet (Dan Leno certainly did and George Robey actually got to play Falstaff on film). Yet

reducing high art to low art was in essence just another part of the Music Hall tradition of deflation and behind it often lay a presumption that something pretentious needed bringing down to earth.

Today that attitude towards Shakespeare has disappeared since for many years both the legitimate theatre and the popular culture have seen the Bard as fair game for both radical reinterpretation and comic inspiration. *Richard III* and *The Merchant Of Venice* are routinely explored in modern dress or transplanted to alien periods in productions that usually have a political agenda. *Romeo and Juliet* was reinvented as a grittily romantic Broadway stage musical (*West Side Story*, 1957) and a Venice Beach-set teen movie (*William Shakespeare's Romeo + Juliet*, 1996); the play even fuelled an evocative Dire Straits pop song ('Romeo and Juliet', 1980). In fact the breezy parody featured here—'The Music-Hall Shakespeare' written in the early 19th century—might find its closest latter-day equivalent in another 1980 pop song, B. A. Robertson's gloriously cheesy 'To Be Or Not To Be'. This features outrageously contrived

rhymes ('Barbadian' forcibly matched to 'Stratford-on-Avian') and breezy observations on some ambiguous Shakespearean plotlines (e.g.'Who cares if Hammy made it with his ma?').

The lyric to 'The Music-Hall Shakespeare' was written by Worton David (who also wrote 'Hello, Hello, Who's Your Lady Friend' with Bert Lee) and the music was by Harry Fragson (who would come to an end worthy of an Edwardian melodrama when he was shot by his elderly father in the Paris flat they shared in 1913). The singer was Emil Clare and his performance recasts, in turn, a soliloquy, a scene, and a character from three plays by Shakespeare. Presenting potted accounts of Shakespeare's originals (Henry VIII gets in on a technicality but does not seem to be an obvious choice), Clare sings the adapted versions to the melodies of various other Music Hall songs all framed within this one. The familiarity and appositeness of those songs would have added an extra frisson of enjoyment for contemporary audiences. Shakespeare was to be targeted again in the halls by William Hargreaves, who in 1920 wrote a song about a Music Hall comedian appearing in *Macbeth* at the Old Bedford Music Hall in Camden Town's Mornington Crescent. In the song he affected to believe the play 'To me lacked both polish and tone' and the lyric also contains two memorable internally rhyming couplets: 'acted so tragic the house rose like magic/The audience yelled "You're sublime"/They made me a present of Mornington Crescent/They threw it a brick at a time'.

UNDER

THE

Influence

Songs About Drinking

If the drinking population is divided into two camps — those who use booze and those who let it use them — then this song collection represents both. True, Gus Elen's ''Arf A Pint Of Ale' tends to get dramatically topped up as the song moves into its conclusion, but in essence this is the viewpoint of the amiable steady drinker who sees ale as a constant benign companion to food rather than as a binge accessory. 'Down At The Old Bull And Bush' also belongs to the sociable camp where drink oils the wheels and loosens the joints in a cheerful social atmosphere. 'Don't Go Out To-night, Dear Father' strikes a more pleading tone that suggests father will not come home pleasantly buzzed but in an altogether more malevolent mood…if he comes home at all. 'I'm One of the Ruins That Cromwell Knocked About a Bit' tells much the same story with the added pathos of self-recognition.

'ARF A PINT OF ALE
Sung by Gus Elen.

Allegro moderato

I hate those chaps what talks a-bout the things what they like to drink Such as
tea and cor-fee, co-coa and milk. Why, of such things I nev-er think. I'm
plain in me hab-its and plain in me food and what I says is this: That the
man what drinks such rub-bish with his meals, Well I al-ways give him a miss.

Chorus
Now, for break-fast I nev-er thinks of 'av-ing tea, I likes me 'arf a pint of
ale. At din-ner I likes a lit-tle bit of meat, And
'arf a pint of ale. At tea I likes a

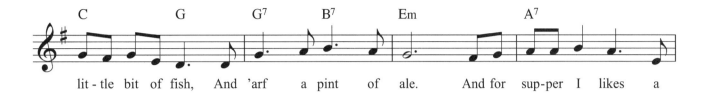

lit - tle bit of fish, And 'arf a pint of ale. And for sup-per I likes a

crust of bread and cheese, And a pint and an 'arf of ale.

Verse 1

I hate those chaps what talks about
the things what they likes to drink
Such as tea and corfee, cocoa and milk.
Why, of such things I never think.
I'm plain in me habits and plain in me food
And what I says is this:
That the man what drinks such rubbish
with his meals,
Well—I always gives him a miss. ▶

Chorus
Now, for breakfast I never thinks of 'aving tea,
I likes me 'arf a pint of ale.
At dinner I likes a little bit of meat,
And 'arf a pint of ale.
At tea I likes a little bit of fish,
And 'arf a pint of ale.
And for supper I likes a crust of bread and cheese,
And a pint and a narf of ale.

Verse 2
Now this is 'ow I looks at it
and I think you'll agree with me,
I never seen a man get drunk in me life
on cocoa, corfee or tea.
You think I'd pay one and eight a pound for tea —
Why the thought makes me feel queer!
When I think of what you gets
for another two and six —
Such a pretty little barrel of beer.

Chorus
(As before, but last line: And a gallon and a narf of ale.*)*

Verse 3
Now folks what drinks such stuff
as that are always lookin' pale;
They've pains in their tummies
and they've pains in their back,
But I never have a pain with ale.
I always feels happy and I always feels right
When I've had a glass or two,
So why should I drink corfee or tea,
when there's plenty of ale —
would you?

Chorus
(As before, but last line: And a barrel and a narf of ale.*)*

The grandly named Ernest Augustus Elen hailed from Pimlico but found fame as Gus Elen, the Coster Comedian, singing East End songs in a Cockney accent. Pimlico in those days had rather less valuable real estate than it does today and Elen's own upbringing was not at all dissimilar from the one he portrayed on stage. Previously he had entertained in a variety of roles and venues, but in 1891 at the age of 29 he made his debut in Music Hall launching his most successful incarnation, the droll costermonger. ''Arf A Pint Of Ale' stands in direct contrast to the professional affectations of the *Lions Comique* like George Leybourne and Alfred Vance who imitated privileged men with their paeans to champagne. Nor does it share much with rousing celebrations like 'Beer, Beer, Glorious Beer' which sound to have something of the fervour of religious conversion about them. Instead ''Arf A Pint Of Ale' is presented by Elen, in a theatrical cockney twang, with sweet reasonableness as the only suitable complement to any meal, be it breakfast, dinner, tea or supper. The song, written by Charles Tempest, has a splendid emotional certaintly about it, despite its decidedly shaky logic. Dating from an age long before the notion of counting alcoholic units existed, the lyric recommends a daily intake of ale that varies from three pints to nine and a half (the variation occurs when the repeated last verse recommends a gallon and a half instead of a pint and a half).

It is a down-to-earth song—ale is for supping, not for discussing. The singer ridicules affected preoccupations as to the relative merits of tea, coffee, cocoa and milk, beverages which he dismisses out of hand on the grounds that no one ever got drunk on them. ''Arf a Pint of Ale' remains a particularly neat and compact song, and its chorus, helped by the variations of its final lines, makes a telling climax to each verse; the total effect is particularly well ordered. Contemporary audiences might not have taken its dietary message much more seriously than we would today, but as an exercise in someone's unshakeable belief in a principle which he claims all the evidence supports even when it doesn't, it is a satisfying and monitory piece.

DON'T GO OUT TO-NIGHT, DEAR FATHER

Words by M.E. Golding. Music by W.L. Thompson.
Version © Copyright: 1925, Chapman and Hall.

Verse 1

Don't go out to-night, dear father,	**Tell them, too, of darling Willie,**
Don't refuse this once, I pray;	**Him we all so much do love,**
Tell your comrades mother's dying,	**How his little form is drooping**
Soon her soul will pass away;	**Soon to bloom again above.**

Chorus

Don't go out to-night, dear father;
Think, oh think, how said 'twill be
When the angels come to take her,
Papa won't be there to see.

Verse 2

Tell me that you love dear mamma,
Lying in that cold, cold room,
That you don't love your comrades better,
Cursing there in that saloon.
Oh, dear father, do not leave us,
Think, oh think, how sad 'twill be,
When the angels come to take her,
Papa won't be there to see.

Verse 3

Morning found the little pleader
Cold and helpless on the floor,
Lying where he madly struck her
On that chilly night before;
Lying there, with hands uplifted,
Feebly uttering words of prayer;
Heavenly Father, please forgive him,
Reunite us all up there.

Sometimes Music Hall's repertoire seemingly comprises almost exclusively boisterous, comic or novelty numbers. Yet it featured in its early days a number of deadly serious songs quite devoid of irony or any built-in self-mockery. Temperance songs, of which 'Don't Go Out To-night, Dear Father' is one of the best known, might then hardly seem appropriate to the ebullient atmosphere of the halls but they were performed there in the early days and they were accepted for what they were. In later years such songs might be reprised in a parodic spirit, their unrelieved depths of despair (not to mention the odd infelicitous line like

'Morning found the little pleader / Cold and helpless on the floor') finally being seen as too much to take seriously. It was also not unknown for parodies sometimes to be written in immediate response and Music Hall audiences also enjoyed these for what they were. The originals, though, for a brief time in their own day gave precise expression to something that was held to be significant by many and in doing so they more or less disqualified themselves from being relevant in any other age. 'Don't Go Out To-Night, Dear Father', written by M. E. Golding and W. L. Thompson, is representative of just one group of Victorian songs that dealt with morbid subjects. Others often seemed to savour the demise of delicate damsels in rather too much detail. One such unfortunate girl, named Lily Dale, was commemorated in H. S. Thompson's 1850 song with lines like these:

'Her cheeks, that once glowed with the rose tint of health
By the hand of disease had turned pale
And the death damp was on the pure white brow
Of my poor lost Lilly Dale.'

Too pathetic? Perhaps, but the novelist Anthony Trollope was so affected by the song that he, so to speak, resurrected the corpse to create a character with her name in his 1864 novel in the Barchester Chronicles series, *The Small House At Allington*. 'Don't Go Out To-Night, Dear Father' is not associated with any particular singer: it was part of the Victorian musical furniture and accordingly used by many, a song of open and unapologetic emotion artlessly expressed.

DOWN AT THE OLD BULL AND BUSH

Sung by Florrie Forde.

Words and Music by Harry Von Tilzer, Andrew Stirling, Percy Kron & Russell Hunting.
© Copyright 1903 Harry Von Tilzer Music Publishing Company.
Redwood Music Limited/Henrees Music Co.
All Rights Reserved. International Copyright Secured.

Moderato

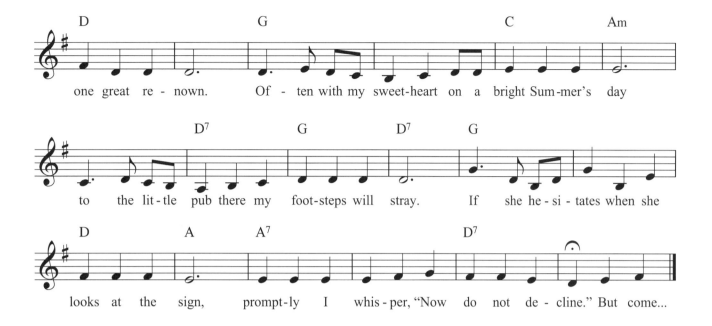

one great re - nown. Of - ten with my sweet-heart on a bright Sum-mer's day

to the lit - tle pub there my foot-steps will stray. If she he - si - tates when she

looks at the sign, prompt-ly I whis - per, "Now do not de - cline." But come...

Chorus 1

But come, come, come and make eyes at me,
Down at 'The Old Bull And Bush'.
Come, come, have some port wine with me,
Down at the 'The Old Bull And Bush'.
Hear the little German band,
Just let me hold your hand dear.
Do, do come and have a drink or two
Down at 'The Old Bull And Bush'.

Verse 1

Talk about the shade of the sheltering palm,
Praise the bamboo tree with its wide
spreading charm.
There's a little nook down near old
Hampstead Town.
You know the place:
It has one great renown.
Often with my sweetheart on a bright
Summer's day,
To the little pub there my footsteps will stray.
If she hesitates when she looks at the sign,
Promptly I whisper, "Now do not decline."

Chorus 2

But come, come, come and make eyes at me,
Down at 'The Old Bull And Bush'.
Come, come, have some port wine with me,
Down at the 'The Old Bull And Bush'.
Hear the little German band,
Just let me hold your hand dear.
Do, do come and have a drink or two
Down at 'The Old Bull And Bush'.

Chorus 3

Come, come, come and make eyes at me,
Down at 'The Old Bull And Bush'.
(da, da, da, da, da)
Come, come, have some port wine with me,
Down at 'The Old Bull And Bush', Bush, Bush.
Hear the little German band,
(la, la, la, la, la, la)
Just let me hold your hand dear.
Do, do come and have a drink or two,
Down at 'The Old Bull And Bush', Bush, Bush!

Everyone agrees that the Music Hall favourite 'Down At The Old Bull And Bush' was written to celebrate a venerable pub of that name located near London's Hampstead Heath. The tavern that once welcomed artist and social critic William Hogarth still stands, although it is now a gastropub that went non-smoking long before English law required it to do so. Most people associate the well-built Australian chanteuse Florrie Forde with popularising the song, although Kate Carney, who sang 'Are We To Part Like This, Bill?', also performed it. What no one seems very clear about are the circumstances of its authorship. Four names are involved and none is British. Percy Krone was an Australian who is credited with having written the song when he was in England; American Russell Hunting was a major figure in sound recording at the end of the 19th century and subsequently brought his expertise to Britain (preceded by his colourful reputation for having committed to record some salacious comic songs that earned him a brief prison sentence in America); finally Andrew B. Sterling and Henry (Harry) Von Tilzer was a successful American songwriting partnership whose connections with Britain in general and London in particular seem nebulous. All four are credited with writing this fairly simple song. We do know that the celebrated Hampstead pub gained a music licence in 1867, that 'Down At The Old Bull And Bush' was written some time later (some say prompted by the pub's popularity with Cockneys who would make it a day-trip destination), and that it cemented Florrie Forde's already considerable fame. She began recording in 1903 and went on to record hundreds of songs until the mid-1930s.

One line in the song invites patrons to 'hear the little German Band', perhaps a surprising inclusion for a song of the early 20th century, although hardly out of keeping with the international flavour of this supposedly British drinking anthem. Like many histories concerning (and perhaps embellished in) drinking places, this all sounds slightly implausible, yet the song, like the pub, has endured. In its modern sophisticated guise the Bull and Bush would not have been recognised by those Edwardian cockneys, but their spirit lives on in the song with those raucous singalong interjections ('Dah-dah-dah-dah-dah-dah-da!') of the song. Meanwhile the site of the pub's own planned underground railway station still exists as a ghostly excavation, even though only the platforms were ever built. When she died, larger-than-life Florrie Forde, like Marie Lloyd, got her own requiem from a famous poet, in this case Louis MacNiece:

'With an elephantine shimmy and a sugared wink
She threw a trellis of Dorothy Perkins roses
Around an audience come from slum and suburb
And weary of the tea-leaves in the sink'.

IT'S A BIT OF A RUIN THAT CROMWELL KNOCKED ABOUT A BIT

Sung by Marie Lloyd.

Words by Harry Bedford and Terry Sullivan. Music by Harry Bedford.

Verse

I'm very fond of ruins, and ruins I love to scan.
You'd say I'm fond of ruins if you saw my old man.
I went out in the country for a stroll the other day
'Cause I like to study history and pubs along the way.
I came across an abbey that was toppled, all of it,
It seemed the relic of a bygone day.
A gentleman said, "What it is"
I said, "Excuse me Sir"
I tell you about it if I may:

Chorus

It's a bit of ruin that Cromwell knocked about a bit,
Bit of a ruin that Cromwell knocked about a bit.
In the gay old days there used to be some doing.
No wonder that the poor old abbey went to ruin.
And those who study ev'rything and shout of it,
And you can bet your life there isn't a doubt of it.
'Cause outside the Cromwell Arms last Saturday night,
I was one of the ruins that Cromwell knocked about a bit.

*Marie Lloyd, with husband
Bernard Dillon.*

The Oxford Dictionary of National Biography notes that Marie Lloyd's performances 'articulated the disappointments of life, especially for working-class women'. Perhaps the word 'articulated' should be replaced with the phrase 'bounced off' because Marie Lloyd was no solemn messenger of disappointment, more a lively commentator on the tragi-comic outcomes of best-laid plans gone awry. She played the dizzy London girl who somehow found herself stranded on Crewe railway station instead of in Birmingham. She impersonated the penniless Music Hall singer in love with the boy in the balcony who is even poorer than she is. She was the wife somehow separated from husband and her chattels during a house move, left behind clutching a birdcage. Finally and tragically, she became associated with a drunken woman in a song that she never recorded but that will always be remembered as the last one she would ever sing.

'It's A Bit of a Ruin That Cromwell Knocked About A Bit,' written by Harry Bedford and Terry Sullivan, seeks to pull off the same kind of trick as Murray and Weston's 'I'm Henery The Eighth I Am' by working backwards from an intriguing title.

Over time the title became adjusted in the popular imagination to 'I'm One Of The Ruins...' to match its final lines. During the course of the English Civil War, Oliver Cromwell's Puritan forces had certainly left their share of ruined buildings dotted around the nation, but the Oliver Cromwell referred to here is a public house named after him and the ruin that totters out of it is a woman who has simply had too much to drink, probably not for the first time.

By her final performance, Marie Lloyd was also drinking too much in response to the violence of her failed third marriage to the unpleasant-sounding Bernard Dillon, an Irish jockey. When Marie Lloyd died, T. S. Eliot wrote an appreciation of her that included the following: 'The attitude of audiences toward Marie Lloyd was different from their attitude toward any other of their favourites of that day, and this difference represents the difference in her art. No other comedian succeeded so well in giving expression to the life of that audience, in raising it to a kind of art. It was, I think, this capacity for expressing the soul of the people that made Marie Lloyd unique, and that made her audiences, even when they joined in the chorus, not so much hilarious as happy.'

A publicity shot of Marie Lloyd whose fame reached New York where her racy reputation preceded her.

Fall

MARIE LLOYD

949 BROADWAY N.Y.

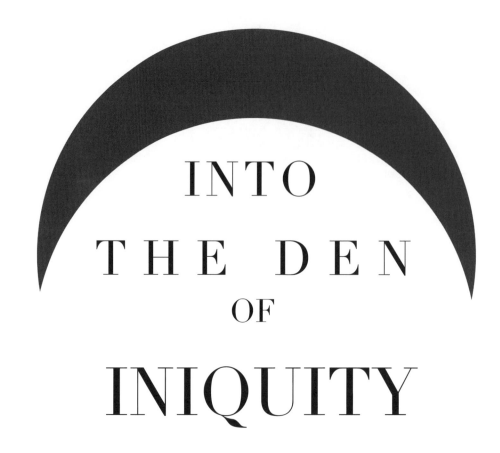

INTO

THE DEN

OF

INIQUITY

Songs of
Innocents Abroad

The virgin from the countryside adrift in London was a frequent Music Hall motif, sometimes surfacing in songs where it was not even the main theme. As often as not, however, it provided the central story of a song. It was not the only Victorian scenario about the trusting provincial at the mercy of an exploitative metropolis. George Formby, Sr. built an entire Music Hall persona on an image of a credulous and unadventurous northerner serially disadvantaged by a sophisticated and venal London.

The fact that the man behind the persona could have bought and sold the con men in his songs many times over only went to show that he was far from being the fool he portrayed. Gracie Fields' 'Heaven Will Protect An Honest Girl' adds practical advice to trust in heaven, and Vesta Victoria's undraped model in 'It's Alright In The Summertime', though no ingénue, is slow to catch on that her Royal Academy painter husband is at least as much of an exploiter as an artist.

HEAVEN WILL PROTECT
AN HONEST GIRL
Sung by Gracie Fields.

Words by R.P. Weston and Bert Lee. Music by Harris Weston.
© Copyright: 1933, Francis, Day & Hunter, Ltd.
All Rights Reserved. International Copyright Secured.

Andante moderato

On the day I left the vil - lage, my dear mo - ther whis - pered, "Nell, Take this

piece of bread and drip - ping and your fare_____ And re -

-mem - ber when in Lon - don, though you're just a ser - vant gel, you're a

blond, the sort that gen - tle - men en - snare._____ With your

youth and fa - tal beau - ty, When you get to Wa - ter - loo, There'll be

crowds of dukes and mil - lion - aires all wait - ing there for you.

Chorus

But Heav-en will pro-tect an hon-est gel_____ An an-gi-el will guard you lit-tle Nell._____ When these rich men tempt you, Nel-ly, with their spark-el-ling Mos-el-ly, Say "Nay Nay!" and do be ve-ry care-fu-el!_____ And if some old bloat-ed blas-é rou-é swell_____ Says, "I'll kiss you, we're a-lone in this ho-tel."_____ Breathe a prayer he shall not do it And then biff him with the cru-et, Then Heav-en will pro-tect an hon-est gel!_____

Verse 1

On the day I left the village, my dear Mother whispered, "Nell,
Take this piece of bread and dripping and your fare,
And remember when in London, though you're just a servant gel,
You're a blonde, the sort that gentleman ensnare.
With your youth and fatal beauty, when you get to Waterloo,
There'll be crowds of dukes and millionaires all waiting there for you—but"

Chorus 1

"Heaven will protect an honest gel,
an an-gi-el will guard you, little Nell.
When these rich men tempt you, Nelly,
With their spark-el-ling Moselly,
Say 'Nay-nay!' and do be very care-fu-el!
And if some old bloated blasé roué swell
Says 'I'll kiss you, we're alone in this hotel,'
Breathe a prayer he shall not do it
And then biff him with the cruet,
Then Heaven will protect an honest gel!"

Verse 2

When I got to wicked London in my little clogs and shawl,
And my bit of bread and dripping in my hand,
I went up to that big Lifeguard on his horse outside Whitehall,
And I asked him to direct me to the Strand.
But he didn't even answer he just sat there with his sword,
In a helment that had whiskers on, so I said "Thank the Lord—for:"

Chorus 2

"Heaven will protect an honest gel,"
And I reached Piccadilly safe and well.
There I saw a red light showing,
But across I started going,
When a P'liceman pulled me back I nearly fell.
"You're a silly little fool," he starts to yell,
"Don't you know what that red light means?" I said, "Well,
Red's for danger, if you please sir,
But don't switch it on for me, sir,
'Cause Heaven will protect an honest gel!"

Optional second verse chorus
(or first chorus of third verse if three verses are used):

Heaven will protect an honest gel,
That night I got a job at some hotel,
But the chef was most improper
For he sat me on the copper
And said, "Kiss me or I'll boil you, little Nell."
But I slapped him on the face—and in I fell,
And I came up for the third time with a yell,
"In the soup I'm going to simmer,
But I'll come out clean and slimmer,
For Heaven will protect an honest gel!"

Verse 3
I wandered round Li-cester Square from six o'clock till nine,
But no millionaire came tempting me to stray,
"If he does", I thought, "I'll let him take me to the Ritz to dine,
Then I'll gollop up his tripe and run away."
Eeh by gum! I did feel hungry! Eeh! I hadn't had a bite
Since my bit of bread and dripping, and I knew that Ma was right—for:"

Chorus 3
Heaven will protect an honest gel.
Next day I pawned my shawl in Camberwell,
Then my skirt and blouse, I sold 'em
And went tramping back to Oldham;
When a fortnight passed, then I rang at the bell.
"Eeh, but Mother dear," I said, "it's little Nell,
I have lost my sole—my uppers too, as well—
And I've walked home in my undies.
But I'll tell my Class on Sundays
That Heaven will protect an honest gel!"

This rather enjoyable treatment of the hallowed Music Hall theme of the provincial innocent abroad in London was sung by Gracie Fields who had been born above her grandmother's fish and chip shop in Rochdale, Lancashire. Fields appeared intermittently in Music Hall between the wars although her long overlapping career in radio, films, variety, the legitimate theatre, tended to obscure her reputation as a successful late Music Hall act. In many ways it was an ideal medium both for her abrasively chummy style (she genuinely connected with a live audience) and her repertoire, which regularly mixed shameless sentimentality with a down-to-earth puncturing of social pretension. This latter trait became increasingly difficult to sustain as she became a wealthy exile in Italy in later life. By then her career had already suffered somewhat because she left Britain for Canada during the London Blitz, possibly out of concern for her Italian-born husband who risked internment if they stayed in Britain, possibly not. Anyway all this happened after Gracie Fields' inter-war Music Hall stints from which period this inventive little song dates.

Dressed in clogs and shawl, and equipped only with a piece of bread and dripping and her mother's advice, young Nell arrives in London expecting to have to defend her honour from the amorous approaches of dukes, millionaires and roués. They prove thin on the ground although she still sees peril everywhere, not least in a red traffic light on Piccadilly. Perhaps this is because of a red light's traditional association with danger or perhaps Nell is actually aware of the concept of a red light district. She gets a job at a hotel, avoids the advances of a chef, leaves and wanders round Leicester Square almost hoping to be accosted by someone wealthy who will buy her a square meal.

Defeated at last, she pawns most of her clothes and walks hundreds of miles back home in her underwear. She even wears out her clogs, which leads to an execrable pun about having lost her 'sole', an announcement which, considering her half-undressed state, must make her mother wonder whether Heaven actually did protect this particular honest girl.

Left: The young Gracie Fields appeared in the halls from time to time in the 1920s although she was also a revue performer, an entertainer of the troops, the occasional musical film star and latterly a stalwart of variety, radio and television.

IT'S ALRIGHT IN THE SUMMERTIME *Sung by Vesta Victoria.*

Words and Music by Fred Murray and George Everard.

Allegro moderato

My old man is a ve-ry fun-ny chap, He's an ar-tist in the Royal A-

-cad-e-my. He paints pic-tures from morn-ing un-til night

paints 'em with his left hand, Paints 'em with his right. All his sub-jects,

take the tip from me, Are ve-ry, ve-ry "Eve and Ad-am-y," And

I'm the mod-el that has to pose For his pic-tures ev-'ry day.

Chorus

And it's al-right in the sum-mer-time, In the sum-mer-time it's

love-ly! While my old man's paint-ing hard, I'm pos-ing in the

old back yard. But oh, oh! In the win-ter-time It's an-oth-er thing, you

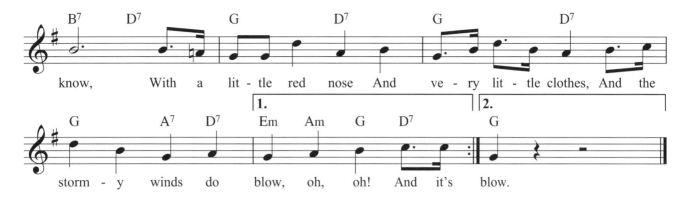

know, With a lit - tle red nose And ve - ry lit - tle clothes, And the

storm - y winds do blow, oh, oh! And it's blow.

Verse 1

My old man is a very funny chap.
He's an artist in the Royal Academy.
He paints pictures from morning until night,
Paints 'em with his left hand, paints 'em with his right.
All his subjects, take the tip from me,
Are very, very "Eve and Adamy",
And I'm the model that has to pose
For his pictures ev'ry day.

Chorus

And it's alright in the summertime,
In the summertime it's lovely!
While my old man's painting hard,
I'm posing in the old backyard.
But oh, oh!
In the wintertime
It's another thing, you know,
With a little red nose,
And very little clothes,
And the stormy winds do blow, oh, oh!

Verse 2

One day I am a Cupid with a dart,
And another day a fairy beautiful.
I pose as Venus arising from the sea,
In the water-butt with the water to my knee.
Then he hangs me out upon the line,
You see, I have to be so dutiful.
As I hang there, oh, he paints me as
An angel in the sky.
My old man, oh, he plays a funny game,
And I've only just begun to tumble him;
All day long he's a running out of paint,
But the paint is whiskey, don't you think it ain't!
These are all the clothes I've got to wear,
But I've made up my mind to humble him;
I'll take a walk up the West one day,
Just dressed up as I am.

197

Born ten years later than Vesta Tilley (who acquired her safety match-inspired stage name as a tot), Victoria Lawrence (a.k.a. Baby Victoria and Little Victoria) probably hi-jacked 'Vesta' when she became an adult performer. Hailing from Yorkshire but reinventing herself as a cockney for the halls, newly christened Vesta Victoria became a star when she was 19 with the 1892 hit 'Daddy Wouldn't Buy Me a Bow Wow'. A little earlier she had been painted by Walter Sickert in a picture titled *Vesta Victoria at the Old Bedford*. Given Sickert's increasingly frequent nomination as the true identity of the serial killer Jack The Ripper, Vesta Victoria may be considered to be one of the more fortunate women to have had an audience with him. It could be fanciful to assume that having her picture painted by a famous artist was what spurred Fred Murray and George Everard to offer Vesta Victoria the song 'It's Alright In The Summertime', a *cri de coeur* from an artist's model, but the coincidence is at least worth noting. Although 'It's Alright In The Summertime' is a diverting enough song, it depends for its effect not so much on the telling of a situation that might engage audiences' sympathy or humour, but on the voyeuristic premise that animated so many Victorian songs: how to evoke female nudity in a pseudo-respectable way. Singing about seaside bathing was one dependable way of inviting audiences to speculate on the undraped female form. The artist's model offered an even better excuse since the

'respectability' of art offered superficial justification for the exercise. No matter if the artist was revealed as a charlatan in the process, guilt had been neatly transferred and a titillating song delivered.

Here most of the lyric is concerned with evoking a near-naked woman being painted *al fresco* by her heavy-drinking artist husband. Even so it displays some deft comic touches in passing. The casual way in which this Royal Academician 'Paints 'em with his left hand, paints 'em with his right' implies more than it says about dismissive popular attitudes to painting. Pressed into service as Cupid, a fairy and Venus arising from a water butt that handily deputises for the sea, the painter's wife can only put up with this sort of discomfort when the weather is warm—hence the title. Hanging her on the clothes line to simulate a floating angel may raise a laugh but it stretches credulity whereas the water butt did not.

The song's improbable tag is that the artist's expensive drinking habit, surreptitiously indulged when he repeatedly disappears because he has 'run out of paint', means that his wife actually does not possess any clothes more substantial than the wisps she is wearing. Her threat to accompany him to the West End *deshabillé* sounds like a slightly desperate invention to end a song that is really little more than a musical version of that other saucy Victorian diversion, the 'what-the-butler-saw' Mutoscope.

Vesta Victoria.

THE MAN WAS A STRANGER
TO ME *Sung by George Formby, Sr.*

Words and Music by T.W. Connor.
© Copyright: Herman Darewski Music Publishing Co. Ltd.
All Rights Reserved. International Copyright Secured.

Patter

Now then Jimmy! That's the conductors name. Get ready now.
We'll start on this note. (*Pause*) Next one!

Verse 1

I never could get on with strangers somehow,
Strange faces I never could see.
Now I met a man in the street t'other day,
But the man was a stranger to me.
He said, "What's the time?", so I pulled out my watch,
I said, "Look for yourself—do, go on—
I don't think it's going." He said, "Yes it is."
In a tick after that it was gone.
As I opened my eyes, I said, "How the time flies!"
My watch in his hand I could see.
And I'd a good mind to ask him to give it me back,
But the man was a stranger to me.

Patter

I think strangers are worse than relations. (*Coughs*)
I'm a little bit tight on chest tonight. Can't understand it
and I've only had one so far. I didn't hear him ask me a second
time. (*Coughs*) I thought as much. Get ready now, lads—second go.

Verse 2

One night up the street I was swanking about,
When a stylish young lady dashed by.
With a heavy portmanteau she'd been for the coal,
I could tell by the piece in her eye.
She said, "Will you carry this for me, please?"
Well, I've carried parcels before
And she was good-looking, so I took on the job,
And I carried it home to her door.
The door opened wide. She said—"Come inside;
Sit down and I'll make you some tea.
Are you fond of pastry?"—and I would have said yes,
But the girl was a stranger to me. ▶

Patter

You was getting in a little bit late, lad, then, weren't you? That last note, weren't you? Well, I'll forgive you. It doesn't matter, I got words out alright. I should think so. I don't know, if they see a fellow dressed up a little bit smart, they're on him. It's not safe for a young lad to be alone. I'm getting a bit ill. Rotten me voice, I know. I bet anybody can tell I'm a bit husky when I'm singing. Are you finished now?

Of all the recordings made by Music Hall stars from the pre-WWI period, few have lasted quite as well as those of the Lancashire comedian, George Formby, Sr. (He was father to the banjolele-flailing George Formby who would become a major stage and screen star in the 1930s and 1940s.) In the very early days of commercial recording, the primitive technical process used seemingly placed an obstacle between performer and listener; yet it is also true that some performers simply suited the medium better than others. George Formby, Sr. was one who suited it.

Formby, Sr. must, in person, have added something to what we can now only hear on records, yet those recordings nearly all project a complete and satisfying performance. Furthermore Formby's diction is very good (except when he is deliberately throwing away lines in mumbled asides). He managed the medium well simply because the confidential style of his approach suited the conditions of recording. A similar phenomenon occurred in radio when informal-sounding singers such as Bing Crosby suited the close-microphone style of singing while the declamatory operatic type of popular singer went out of fashion. In both of the songs by George Formby, Sr. represented here ('We All Went Home In A Cab' is the other), he addresses brief remarks to the musical conductor, commenting on the performance. Also Formby's 'trademark' cough can sometimes be heard on the recorded versions of his songs. The cough was unbidden but he still worked it into the act even though he knew it was a symptom of serious illness (bronchitis, tuberculosis and the 1918 influenza pandemic all contributed to his death in early 1921.)

He hoped to keep going until his son was old enough to earn a living, preferably not on the stage. In fact George Junior would go on the stage and equal his father's fame and fortune, making films as well as records, appearing on TV and giving many live appearances. He would also adopt his father's ruse of appearing almost simple-minded in a good-natured sort of way, milking audience sympathy and equipping himself with an innocently goofy image that came in useful when delivering some of his more risqué lyrics. It was a contrivance, as was his father's guilelessness, but in George Junior's day, greater media exposure made his simpleness of manner look like more of an imposture.

George Formby, Sr.'s ingenuous style projected a more engaging sort of simplicity, and this is demonstrated in 'The Man Was A Stranger To Me'.

In the first verse a strange man gulls him out of his watch and meets no resistance from slow-witted George. In the second verse an attractive young woman picks him up in the street and takes him home, but in politely refusing her coded offer of tea and pastry, he is too innocent to accept or even understand what he is refusing. The song therefore has a pathetic aspect about a life not being fully lived due to paralysing shyness. The loss of a watch may be sad, but his reaction to the veiled offer of sex suggests that he is ill-equipped even to recognise that life is passing him by. The phrase 'The Man Was A Stranger To Me' hints that in his attenuated world only close friends and family are to be trusted; where strangers are involved, exploitation surely follows.

WE ALL WENT HOME IN A CAB
Sung by George Formby, Sr.

Words by Harry Wincott. Music by George Le Brunn.
© Copyright: Herman Darewski Music Publishing Co. Ltd.
All Rights Reserved. International Copyright Secured.

Moderato

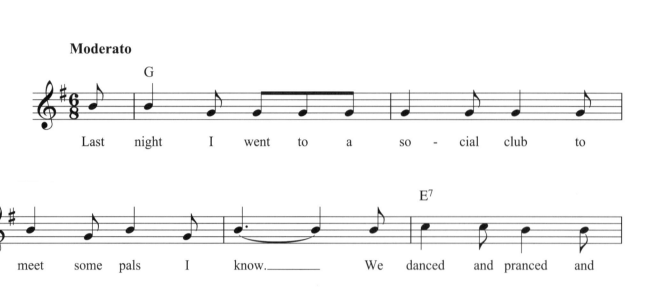

Last night I went to a so - cial club to

meet some pals I know._____ We danced and pranced and

jumped a - bout Un - til it was time to go._____

Chorus

So we all went home in a cab. We

all went home in a cab. The bot - tom fell out, But the

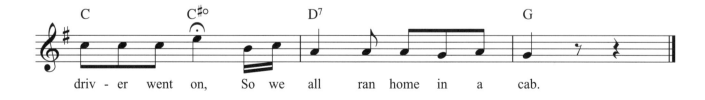

driv - er went on, So we all ran home in a cab.

Patter

Play nice and soft for me and then
you can have one when you're finished.
Get ready—

Verse 1

Last night I went to a social club
To meet some pals I know.
We danced and pranced and
jumped about
Until it was time to go.
So we all went home in a cab,
The bottom fell out,
But the driver went on,
So we all ran home in a cab.

Patter

We did an' all. I never ran faster
in me life. I'll go home no more in cabs.

Verse 2

We went into an ice-cream shop,
Of drinks we had our sup,
With ice-cream, ginger-beer, and pop,
Until I blew us up.
Then we all went home in a tram,
But the guard pushed us off
And we fell on the floor,
So we didn't go home in a tram.

Patter

No we didn't. We went in an ambulance.
I got fast in one o' tramlines and they
had to get me out with a 'airpn.

Verse 3

The other day we all set out
And we felt very fit.
We had champagne, the one chap said,
Let's make a night of it.
And we didn't get 'ome last night,
We didn't get 'ome last night.
We'd some business to do
With a man dressed in blue.
So we didn't go home last night.

Patter

He was a very nice policeman. He
said he'd 've let us go only in their police
station, they have a system and there's no
friendship in business. He put a lovely
pair of bracelets on my wrist and he had
one on his fastened to mine. That was to
stop him running away from me.

Verse 4

Next morning we felt very dry.
We got let off that day.
The first thing that we did you'll bet,
As we got on our way,
We all went into a pub
To get some beer in there,
But it hadn't got strength
To come up the pump,
So we all came out again.

Patter

Think you've had enough now.

George Formby, Sr.—a smart man playing a fool.

In this song George Formby, Sr. was very much the Lancashire Lad playing the provincial come to town. It was entirely consistent with his stage persona of being naively good-natured that he should be a rubberneck in the great metropolis of London and stand amazed at all that went on. It was an act but an act rooted in reality. As a provincial Music Hall artist he was different and he did see things differently. Out of his perspective sprang a gentle, ironical mocking of the pretentions of the London that had given birth to songs about raffish boulevardiers, and must therefore, from his perspective, be somehow false. This did not exclude his stage character from temptation even though the limitations of his idea of having a good time were clear. His song 'Playing The Game In The West' depicts him having had a thrilling time in London's West End but being left with only one of the two shillings he started out with…but because it is his night out, he still has no intention of returning home before a quarter to ten. 'We All Went Home In A Cab' is a good example of the kind of good-natured mismatch of expectation and reality of which Formby was a master. The first verse describes his party's energetic dancing at a social club; getting into the spirit of life Up West, they indulge in the rare luxury of a ride home in a cab.

Perhaps as the result of overloading, the bottom of the vehicle falls out so that the occupants have to run inside the cab to keep up with the enclosure—a somewhat compromised luxury. Like most of Formby's songs, this one is not particularly witty nor does it make fanciful use of language, but it does express an irrepressible and consistent good humour in the face of adversity.

Formby's songs can be seen as a musical continuum that reveals his character incrementally rather than a repertoire of stand-alone numbers each with a life of its own. George Formby, Sr. does seem to have been an unpretentious fellow and it is a shame that the great days of Music Hall were already over when he died. Even so he left a very substantial amount of money. His son—a less obviously likeable man despite (or perhaps because of) his aggressively mugging style of friendliness—became a major star in his own right and thanks to films and TV reached a much wider audience than his father ever did.

YOUNG MEN TAKEN IN AND DONE FOR

Sung by Dan Leno.

Moderato

As smart a man as ev - er lived was I when in my prime, Un -

-til I met Miss Lu - cy Jaggs, she knocked me out of time. I

called there for a - part - ments for I'd no - ticed once or twice, A

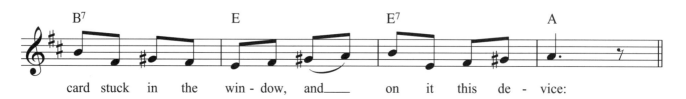

card stuck in the win - dow, and___ on it this de - vice:

Tempo di Marcia

Chorus

"Young men tak - en in and done for," Oh! I nev - er thought that she, The

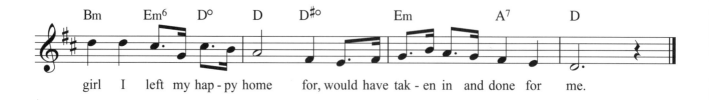

girl I left my hap - py home for, would have tak - en in and done for me.

208

Verse 1

As smart a man as ever lived was I when in my prime,
Until I met Miss Lucy Jaggs, she knocked me out of time.
I called there for apartments, for I'd noticed once or twice,
A card stuck in the window, and on it this device:

Chorus

"Young men taken in and done for,"
Oh! I never thought that she,
The girl I left my happy home for,
Would have taken in and done for me.

Verse 2

Being a lonely single man, I wanted lodgings bad,
So Lucy Jaggs's mother then soon showed me what she had.
I'd stayed there above a week when Lucy came to me
And fondly kissed me on my cheek, then sat me on her knee.

Verse 3

Of course, just like a stupid, I must go and tie the knot
That brings us bliss and happiness — but that's all tommy rot.
I don't believe my wife loves me, it's the truth I'm telling you.
A wife can't love her husband much
if she beats him black and blue.

Harry King's song deserves special applause for its title alone. A clever double pun, both its literal and hidden meanings would have been instantly clear to contemporary audiences. 'Young Men Taken In' was a landlady's familiar phrase of the day that indicated a male lodger would be welcome (not always the case when there were daughters in the house). 'Doing For' was also familiar phrase meaning that cleaning and perhaps washing services would also be provided. As it comes out here, the juxtaposition of these offers predicts that the young man in question will get the promised services while simultaneously being duped and defeated. In the Music Hall, as in life, marriage itself was sometimes treated in a hard-headed or even ironic fashion (although not always with such pleasing linguistic dexterity as here). 'The Future Mrs 'Awkins' was unusual in that, although down-to-earth, it was also tender without becoming unduly sentimental. 'Young Men Taken In And Done For', on the other hand, shows marriage as pragmatic goal strategically attained by two women—landlady and daughter—probably both of whom are smarter than the groom designate.

A number of songs of the time referred to men in lodgings, often the result of their leaving home to be near to their jobs. Rather like mixed bathing, the lodging house could provide an instant setting of intimacy in which romance (and sometimes unwanted pregnancies) might ensue.

In a companion song where the lodger is the manipulator, Vesta Victoria sang of a lodger who was 'such a nice young man' as to sound too good to be true, recommending himself to family members by obsequious ingratiation. His agenda is never revealed but looks likely to result in marriage to the young woman whose first instinct was to tell him to go away.

'Young Men Taken In And Done For' presents an ironic picture of deception and disillusionment and it suited Dan Leno's style admirably. After its clever title the song's verbal inventiveness falls off a bit and we might have liked to hear more about this contrived union. As it is, the song is brief and ends rather bleakly with the admission that 'I don't believe my wife loves me'—a conclusion reached by the lodger with characteristic slowness since his new bride is already subjecting him to physical attacks.

JUST FOR A

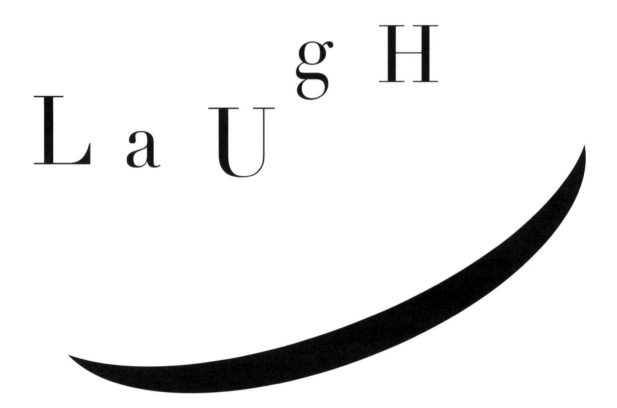

L a U ^g H

Novelty Songs

Some Music Hall songs existed mainly to project the personality of a star comic performer who would use them sparingly in an act that involved a lot of patter. Sometimes these would be nothing more than novelty songs, innocent of any deeper meaning. George Robey's 'Prehistoric Man' routine was one such. Try as the humourless academic might, it's hard to give songs or acts like 'Prehistoric Man' a semiotic reading. Other performers delighted in similarly wacky scenarios such as the fate of the Irish/Indian nobleman and his betrothed in 'I've Got Rings On My Fingers'. Sometimes the songwriter might start with an attention-grabbing title which the lyric would then seek to justify. 'I'm Henery The Eighth I Am' is an inspired example of that approach. Even when such songs touch on a serious topic, seriousness is rarely what they are about. They are comic art for comic art's sake, resisting interpretation and intended simply to entertain by means of rhyme rather than reason. As such they were surely as true as any other type of song to the founding spirit of the Music Hall in which escapism was one of the founding principles.

A LITTLE BIT OF CUCUMBER Sung by Harry Champion.

Written and Composed by T.W. Connor.
© Copyright: 1915, Francis, Day & Hunter.
All Rights Reserved. International Copyright Secured.

Allegro moderato

I was weaned on cu - cum - ber And on my wed - ding day, Sit - ting down to sup - per when the guests had gone a - way, My old darl - ing said to me, "You must be hun - gry, Joe!" "Fan - cy?" I said, "Fan - cy! Don't you know?

Chorus

I like pick - led on - ions, I like pic - ca - lil - li. Pick - led cab - bage is al - right with a bit of cold meat on Sun - day night. I can go ter - mar - toes, But what I do pre - fer, Is a lit - tle bit of cu - cum - cu - cum - cu - cum, Lit - tle bit of cu - cum - ber."

Verse 1

I was weaned on cucumber
And on my wedding day,
Sitting down to supper when
The guests had gone away,
My old darling said to me,
"You must be hungry, Joe!
What is it you fancy?" I Said,
"Fancy! Don't you know?"

Chorus

"I like pickled onions,
I like piccalilli.
Pickled cabbage is alright
With a bit of cold meat on
Sunday night.
I can go termartoes,
But what I do prefer,
Is a little bit of
cu-cum-cu-cum-cu-cum,
Little bit of cucumber."

Verse 2

I went flying in the air
With my old college chum.
Suddenly he said to me,
"We're bound for kingdom come!
Is there anything on your mind
Before you wear a crown?"
I began to shake and said,
"Write this confession down:"

Verse 3

To the Lord Mayor's Banquet I
Got in one foggy day.
When I saw the grub it took
My appetite away:
"Sparrowgrass" and chaffinches,
And pigs-head stuffed with jam!
I said to the waiter there,
'You don't know who I am!'"

Verse 4

Sev'ral years of married life
Have brought me lots of joys.
I don't know how many girls,
I think it's fourteen boys.
When the last one came to town
It nearly turned my head.
It was marked with a cucumber,
And the first words that it said,
Were:

Chorus

Harry Champion, born in Shoreditch in 1866, sang a wide variety of Music Hall songs but seemed to have a special fondness for songs about food, particularly working-class favourites such as pickled onions, hot meat pies, saveloys, trotters, tripe, onions, and even baked sheep's heart. His little bit of cucumber sounds rather tame in this otherwise robust roster of foodstuffs but it seems safe to assume that T.W. Connor, who wrote the song, was more attracted by the phonetic possibilities of the word 'cucumber' than what it described; Harry Champion could be relied upon to give any lyric a suitably bracing reading. The song dates from the beginning World War I and boasts a chorus that fairly rattles along, its words lending themselves to various percussive variations ('Cu-cum-you-come-cu-cum' was one popular variation that might not be so readily attempted today in the unlikely event that anyone should attempt to revive this song) while the verses frankly do little more than mark time until the chorus comes round again.

It does not seem to be one of Connor's most carefully thought out songs since the final verse about weaning a son on cucumber sounds as if it should precede an earlier one about the singer going flying and assuming that he was about to meet his maker, his 'last meal' craving for cucumber undiminished by mortal fear.

If there is any sort of moral in such an essentially unpretentious and crowd-pleasing number, it seems to share it with all the other food-themed Harry Champion songs. 'A Little Bit Of Cucumber' presents simple working-class food (pickled onions, piccalilli, tomatoes, cabbage and cold meat) as being somehow superior to the prissy and exotic tastes of the effete upper classes ('sparrowgrass and chaffinches / and pig's head stuffed with jam'). In fact most of Champion's songs wholeheartedly celebrate the pleasures of the simple life, and to this extent they find echoes in the songs of Marie Lloyd ('A Little Of What You Fancy Does You Good') and Nellie Wallace ('Let's Have A Tiddley At The Milk Bar') not to mention Gus Elen's ''Arf A Pint Of Ale' and all that went with it.

Harry Champion in later years,
still happy to revisit his glory days.

I'M HENERY THE EIGHTH, I AM
Sung by Harry Champion.

Words and Music by R. Weston & F. Murray.
© Copyright 2013 Dorsey Brothers Music Limited.
All Rights Reserved. International Copyright Secured.

Allegro moderato

Verse C

You don't know who you're look-ing at; now have a look at me! I'm a bit of a nob, I am, be-

D G C F

-long to ro-yal-ty. I'll tell you how it came a-bout; I mar-ried Wi-dow Burch,

C G C Am

I was King of Eng-land when I tod-dled out of church. Out-side the peo-ple start-ed

E Am Dm G

shout-ing, "Hip, hoo-ray!" Said I, "Get down up on your knees, it's Co-ro-na-tion Day!"

Chorus C F C

I'm He-ne-ry the Eighth, I am, He-ne-ry the Eighth I am, I am!

D G

I got mar-ried to the wi-dow next door, she'd been mar-ried se-ven times be-fore.

C G F C

Ev - 'ry one was a He-ne-ry. She would-n't have a Wil-lie or a Sam. I'm her

F C G C

eighth old man named He-ne-ry, He-ne-ry the Eighth, I am!

Verse 1

I let 'The Duke of Cumberland',
A pub up in the town.
Soon with one or two moochers
I was holding up 'The Crown'.
I sat upon the bucket
That the car-men think their own;
Surrounded by my subjects
I was sitting on the throne.
Out came the pot-man, saying,
"Now go home to bed!"
Said I, "Now say another word,
And off 'll go your head!"

Chorus

I'm Henery the Eighth, I am,
Henery The Eighth I am, I am!
I got married to the widow next door,
She'd been married seven times before.
Ev'ry one was a Henery.
She wouldn't have a Willie or a Sam.
I'm her eighth old man named Henery,
Henery the Eighth, I am!

Verse 2

The undertaker called
 And to the wife I heard him say
Have you got any orders, mum?
We're very slack today.
I packed up number seven for you
For the golden gates.
Let's have a pound upon account
Of Henery the Eighth."
Oh, when he measured me
With half a yard of string.
I dropped upon me maribound and sang,
"God Save The King"...

Chorus

It was Harry Champion's theme song and one which over the years he was to attempt at ever more breakneck speeds. With music by Fred Murray and lyrics by R. P. Weston 'I'm Henery The Eighth, I Am' is a little masterpiece of the novelty song—repetitive and trite but constructed with brilliant economy and wit. Weston seemed to have a thing about Henry VIII since he also penned 'With Her Head Tucked Underneath Her Arm', a grim little piece about the ghost of Anne Boleyn seeking revenge on Henry upon whose instruction she had been beheaded. Written in 1910, Harry Champion's theme song was to enjoy a long life. Rather against the odds it made No. 1 in the US charts back in August 1965 in a version by Herman's Hermits. The British group were still on a roll from an earlier No. 1 hit and all things British were doing well in the US (The Rolling Stones' '[I Can't Get No] Satisfaction' had preceded Herman's Hermits at the No. 1 slot). In fact another British performer, Joe Brown, had already revived the song in 1961 and still keeps it in his act, occasionally bemoaning its repetitiveness but now unwilling or unable to omit it. Champion's 'A Little Bit Of Cucumber' and 'Have You Paid The Rent?' were respectively a nonsense song and a rather grim topical social refrain ending in an eviction. His Henery (three syllables are necessary to maintain the metre) was a tour de force, a perfect example of an implausible situation being explained with impeccable logic. Everything works backwards from the title and it all fits together without a single wasted word.

Harry Champion retired in 1920 when Music Hall was superseded by Variety, a form not well suited to acts such as his. He started up a taxi service company in Tottenham, north London, which became very successful. Like several old-time Music Hall acts he was granted an Indian summer in the 1930s when he again performed on stage intermittently and, towards the end of the decade, on radio too. He died in 1942 but his theme tune kept going, surviving even the *faux* English-accented mauling Patrick Swayze gave it in *Ghost* and the accolade of a variant version in *The Simpsons* sung by Homer Simpson as homage to Henry VIII, like himself another big eater.

The Holborn Empire Music Hall, London.

I'VE GOT RINGS ON MY FINGERS

Sung by Ellaline Terriss.

Words by R. P. Weston and F. J. Barnes.
Music by Maurice Scott.
© Copyright: 1909, Francis, Day & Hunter, Ltd.
All Rights Reserved. International Copyright Secured.

Allegretto

Now Jim O' Shea was cast a - way up - on an In - dian Isle. The
na - tives there they liked his hair, They liked his I - rish smile, So
made him chief Pan - jan - drum, The Na - bob of them all. They
called him Jij - ji - boo Jhai, And rigged him out so gay, So he
wrote to Dub - lin Bay, To his sweet - heart just to say:
Sure, I've got rings on my fin - gers, bells on my Rose; So
come to your Na - bob, and next Pat - rick's Day, Be
Mis - tress Mum - bo Jum - bo Jij - ji - boo J. O' - Shea.

Verse 1

Now Jim O'Shea was cast away
Upon an Indian Isle.
The natives there they liked his hair,
They liked his Irish smile,
So made him chief Panjandrum,
The Nabob of them all.
They called him Jii-ji-boo Jhai,
And rigged him out so gay,
So he wrote to Dublin Bay,
To his sweetheart, just to say:

Chorus

Sure, I've got rings on my
fingers, bells on my toes,
Elephants to ride upon, my little
Irish Rose;
So come to your Nabob, and next
Patrick's Day,
Be Mistress Mumbo Jumbo
Jij-ji-boo J. O'Shea.

Verse 2

Across the sea went Rose Magee
To see her Nabob grand.
He sat within his palanquin,
And when she kissed his hand,
He led her to his harem,
Where he had wives galore.
She started shedding a tear;
Said he, "Now have no fear,
I'm keeping these wives here
Just for ornament, my dear."

Verse 3

In emerald green he robed his queen,
To share with him his throne.
'Mid eastern charms and waving palms
They'd shamrocks, Irish grown,
Sent all the way from Dublin
To Nabob J. O'Shea.
But in his palace so fine,
Should Rose for Ireland pine,
With smiles her face will shine
When he murmurs, "Sweetheart mine".

Ellaline Terriss (née Lewin) was one of those people whose life seemed touched by the extraordinary at every turn. A dazzlingly pretty and talented woman, she became a famous star of musical comedy in Britain in the late 19th century even though she had been born in the remote location of Port Stanley in the Falkland Islands. Her charismatic father, William Lewin, had been something of an adventurer and he abandoned sheep farming on the islands in the early 1870s soon after Ellaline's birth, moving his family to London. There, in the last of several sweeping changes of career, he became an actor and renamed himself William Terriss. Aged 16, his daughter trod the boards for the first time under the name of Ellaline Terriss in *Cupid's Messenger* at London's Haymarket Theatre. Five years later she married upcoming actor Arthur Seymour Hicks and they became a famous theatrical couple. It was the start of a successful career in Edwardian musical comedy rather than Music Hall, although Ellaline Terriss did appear in a particularly lavish production of the pantomime *Cinderella* the same year she got married. In 1897 came tragedy: colourful to the end, her father was fatally stabbed by a disgruntled actor on his way to the Adelphi Theatre in a case of mistaken identity. Terriss and Hicks received a wave of public sympathy and would remain stars, touring the United States and occasionally staying with W. S. Gilbert at Grims Dyke, his famous Harrow Weald home. 'I've Got Rings On My Fingers' is a cheerful a piece of nonsense that at least sounds like a genuine Music Hall song in that it creates its own self-contained world (if a rather surreal one) rather than being something taken from a musical comedy with a bigger plot. It is not Ellaline Terriss' fingers that bear the rings but those of the hero of the song, an Irishman called Jim O'Shea whose travels have taken him to an 'Indian Isle' where he has been elevated to the office of chief Panjandrum, decked out with rings on his fingers and bells on his toes and given several wives for good measure. He finds no reason in all this exotic good fortune not to invite his sweetheart back in Dublin to join him and share in his new-found prestige, so Rose Magee does just that, becoming a compliant part of this unlikely Irish/Indian dignitary's multicultural world. Understandably unsettled by Jim's grace-and-favour harem, she is reassured by him that the extra wives are 'Just for ornament'. We do not learn whether they lived happily ever after. Ellaline Terriss probably did, appearing in films until 1939 and then having ten more years with Sir Seymour Hicks (he had been knighted in 1934) before he died aged 78. She survived a further 22 years, dying in Richmond, Surrey, at the age of 99 in 1971.

18th December 1901: The actress Ellaline Terriss in a production of the musical dream-play, 'Bluebell In Fairyland'.

PREHISTORIC MAN Sung by George Robey.

Words and Music by Richard Temple, Jr. and C.G. Cotes.
© Copyright: Bowerman & Co.
All Rights Reserved. International Copyright Secured.

Verse 1

I'm really very harmless, no one need have any fears,
Preserv'd in clay you know I lay for twenty thousand years;
I live in a museum and the entrance it is free,
Just walk in at the front door if you want to call on me!

Patter

You see, how I came to be found in this way—I went to sleep one day in a primeval forest. You know what a primeval forest is, don't you? Well, like Epping Forest, only thicker. Well, our forests got so thick, they had to shut some of them up. I suppose I must have slept about twenty thousand years—I couldn't be sure to the minute, you see, my watch stopped before I woke up; anyhow, somebody found me and shipped me over here to the Museum.

Chorus

And I'm on show in the day time, I'm off show at night.
My flint-head spear is polished, and my manners quite;

A Paleolithic, imagine if you can,
A most terrific, though pacific,
Prehistoric Man.
We'd a prehistoric war once, and it was an awful bore
Although we gained the victory, we had to pay the score.
Although the people growled and said the Government was lax.
They put an extra pound of chalk upon the income tax.

Patter

Of course, we didn't have money in those days; they used to pay with lumps of rock! This was a threepenny-piece in my time. So instead of paying our way we used to weigh our pay! (What ho! A prehistoric joke.) Supposing you wanted a drink in those days, you didn't go into a pub and put twopence on the counter. You simply put your fist on the counter. If the landlord had a smaller fist than you, he'd serve you. But, on the other hand, had he a larger fist—Its marvellous how many widows there were in our village. We didn't call each other Percy and Clarence in those days. No Christian names. For instance. I was "He of the auburn hair!" With youthful indiscretion I married ▶

"She of the tireless tongue." I furnished a lovely cave for her, draped with sea-weed and full of "rocking" chairs—you know, more rock than chair. We lived happily together till I found, during my absence, she had been breaking bread with "He of the Knotted Knee". It cost me any amount of rock to keep it out of the papers. I should think I spent the Giant's Causeway on it. Mind you, 1 sympathised with Knotted Knee—he married "She of the Fearful Face". I think he met her at a mask ball. She hadn't got a mask on, but he thought she had, hence the error. Of course, we had pure minds in those days. That's why we went about like this. I was treated very badly at home until my fourteenth birthday. Then father seemed to change toward me. I don't know if it was because I was old enough to fetch his beer or what. I was an awful sport in my days. I won the Stonehenge Waterloo Cup, three

epochs in succession—with my stud of flying alligators. I used to breed them myself—a sort of cross between a wet day and a glow-worm. I used to play football for the Rockoil Ramblers. I was called "He of the Anxious Ankle". We used to have lumps of rock for a football, and when you'd broken ten toes at the game, you were an in-toe-national. I hadn't been playing five minutes before I was an international. They were rough with me. By the time the match finished I was wearing the Blackburn Rovers colours, black and blue stripes—in bruises. We had funny ways of making love then. Supposing two men were in love with one girl, we used to toss for her—not with coins. Oh, no! We used to toss each other over cliffs. Of course, the man who lost was no good to anybody.

Chorus

George Robey, the well-educated man who delighted in patter and whose songs often acted as scene-setters for his act, would deliver various different versions of his songs. It was a characteristic of Music Hall that there was no obligation to create a single word-perfect version of anything since audiences changed nightly and would not be expecting a fixed performance. Recordings offered another incentive to create edited versions of songs, trimmed to suit the optimum playing time of a record. Since some print versions of songs may have been taken from a recording while others reflect a longer published version, there is plenty of room for variation.

A pre-1914 recording of Robey's 'Bang Went The Chance Of A Lifetime' not only shows many verbal changes, but also includes brief patter that does not appear in the printed text. 'Prehistoric Man' is another patter-rich case in point. For this routine Robey dressed himself in a shaggy doormat slung across a naked chest and recalled wearing 'an auburn wig that stuck out all around my face, causing it to look like a picture of the sun at noon'. The song is typical of those Robey used to introduce a character in his act. It serves the purpose of getting him on stage and creating a certain amount of atmosphere. Even in the attenuated version presented here, it is the patter that forms the basis of the act. As Robey also commented: 'The public didn't worry very much about tunes so long as they heard something in the way of "character" or comment on life which made them laugh.' This patter derives its comic tension from the incongruity between down-to-earth realism and patent impossibility, a tension which Robey builds with deceptive ease.

'I suppose I must have slept about twenty thousand years' might get a modest laugh. 'I couldn't be sure to the minute' gets a bigger laugh. 'You see, my watch stopped before I woke up' gets a bigger laugh still because the audience is now warming to this ever more exaggerated conceit.

Even so, on paper, this hardly looks like great comedy, yet we know 'Prehistoric Man' to have been hugely successful. Obviously Robey's personality and sense of timing had much to do with this success and doubtless the prehistoric had a kind of novelty value for audiences in an age when Victorian science was much concerned with re-evaluating man's origins. Yet 'Prehistoric Man' does reveal an enjoyment of fantasy and a playing with words that made demands upon an audience's power to listen and actively imagine the supporting detail of a fantasy.

It is not too fanciful to see Robey's style of humour as a natural precursor to the first generation of British radio shows that made even greater demands on an audience's capacity to pick up rapid and allusive aural descriptions to help them conjure whole comic scenarios. Unknown to today's audiences, BBC radio shows such as *Bandwaggon* (1938—1940) and *ITMA* (1939—1949) started a tradition that would lead to the influential the *Goon Show* (1951—1960) and other comedy formats that depended on absurdity and vivid word-pictures. By the early 1960s a whole generation of British radio listeners could easily envisage 23 Railway Cuttings, East Cheam, the dispiriting fictitious home of Tony Hancock, lugubrious hero of the popular show *Hancock's Half Hour*.

George Robey, who would acquit himself well as a legitimate actor, never let this stop him from embracing over-the-top costumes and make up to add colour to his Music Hall appearances.

SEAWEED _Sung by Fred Earle._

Words and Music by Fred Earle.
© Copyright: Francis, Day & Hunter, Ltd.
All Rights Reserved. International Copyright Secured.

Verse 1

Last summertime I went away to Dover by
the sea
And thought I'd like to bring a bunch of
seaweed home with me.
It tells you if it's going to rain or if it's going
to snow
And with it anyone can tell just what he
wants to know.

Chorus

With my seaweed in my hand I got into
the train;
All the pubs were closed when I got
out again.
I couldn't get a drink, with thirst I thought
I'd die,
And as soon as I touched my seaweed,
I knew it was going to be dry.

Verse 2

Two lovers walked one evening down
a quiet country lane;
The chap was Honest William and the
girl was Mary Jane.
They talked and walked and walked and
talked about their future life;
I heard him say, "I shall be glad when
you're my darling wife".

Chorus

Then he kissed her ruby lips and looked at
her with pride,
Said, "I shall be glad when, darling,
you're my bride.
Tomorrow we'll be wed and then you will
be mine!"
And as soon as I touched my seaweed,
I knew it was going to be fine.

Verse 3

I had a fright some time ago right in the
dead of night;
The missus said, "Wake up you fool,
the house is all alight!"
I quickly tumbled out of bed, though
I could hardly stand,
My seaweed hung upon the wall,
I grabbed it in my hand.

Chorus

And rushed upon the roof, forgot to
take my clothes;
The fireman down below was squirting
with his hose.
He hit me where I stood, right on
the parapet,
And as soon as I touched my seaweed,
I knew it was going to be wet. ▶

Verse 4

One night I felt so cold in bed, I woke
my wife Maria
And said, "I'm going to jump out love, and
light a little fire!"
Then in my nightie I jumped out, quite
balmy on the thatch,
I found the wood, and found the coal, and
then I struck a match.

Chorus

And stood before the fire as happy
as can be;
Soon I felt the warmth round my anatomie.
My shirt was all alight and I'll
forget-me-not
For as soon as I touched my seaweed,
I knew it was going to be hot.

Verse 5

In all my happy married life I'd never
had a row
Till someone put the poison in and things
have altered now.
My wife, when I got into bed the other
Thursday night,
She put her cold feet on my back and
kicked with all her might.

Chorus

And pushed me out of bed, I fell
on to the floor;
She said she wouldn't have me back
there any more.
She took the sheets and quilts, in which
herself she rolled,
And as soon as I touched my seaweed,
I knew it was going to be cold.

The British concept of the traditional seaside was, like the Music Hall, a Victorian invention. Buckets and spades, sandcastles, donkey rides, Punch and Judy as well as fish and chips, ice cream, candy-floss, cockles and whelks all came together at seaside towns which first saw their populations swollen by middle-class holidaymakers thanks to the coming of the railway age. Rail travel was not cheap, so to begin with working-class visitors relied on cheap excursions, organised by Sunday Schools, employers, temperance societies or commercial promoters. From the 1870s onwards, working-class saving schemes funded seaside breaks on various Bank Holidays and by the last quarter of the 19th century many seaside resorts were experiencing an influx of working-class holidaymakers who had increased spending power, especially among young people with wages and few responsibilities. Along with more than a few roués they gave the seaside break a slightly naughty reputation much relished by satirists and comics of the day, not least in the Music Hall. Bathing in particular, with its potential for a sudden liberating co-mingling of scantily dressed men and women, was particularly titillating in an age when formality of dress and behaviour were the social norm. As soon as the seaside became fashionable, it replaced the river as a subject for popular songs. 'Seaweed', written and sung by Fred Earle, the son of Joseph Tabrar who had given us 'He's Going To Marry Mary Ann', is not so much about the seaside as about the must-have seaside souvenir that cost nothing and was supposed to possess climatic predictive powers.

Those powers were assumed to give early indications of imminent rain or dry weather (although the algae in fact does nothing more than absorb moisture in the air when it is present or remain brittle when the air is dry) but Earle's song extends this assumed clairvoyance to predicting all sorts of things, most of them with more than a hint of innuendo. It is a milder forbear of George Formby, Jr.'s 'With My Little Ukulele In My Hand' and builds on the pseudo-science of seaweed weather forecasting to become a themed nonsense song.

YOU'VE GOT A LONG WAY TO GO

Sung by Frank Coyne.

Words and Music by A.J. Mills and F.W. Carter.
© Copyright: Francis, Day & Hunter, Ltd.
All Rights Reserved. International Copyright Secured.

Allegro moderato

One morn-ing in a lit-tle tail-or's shop I saw dis-played___ a

pair of la-dies' bloom-ers, seven and six-pence, rea-dy made;___ I

took my daugh-ter in next day, the fel-low got his tape,___ And

mur-mured as he start-ed put-ting it a-round her shape:___

Chorus

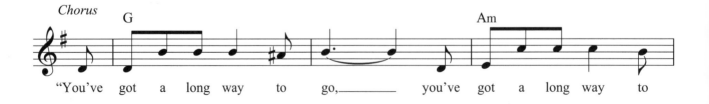

"You've got a long way to go,___ you've got a long way to

go;_____ Oh! What a ter - ri - ble lump of stuff, The

three - yard mea - sure ain't long e - nough; She's ov - er nine - ty

five_____ round her "Se - rag - li - o."_____ To find a pair of

pants to fit her; you've got a long way to go._____

Verse 1

**One morning in a little tailor's shop
I saw displayed
A pair of ladies' bloomers, seven and
sixpence, ready made;
I took my daughter in next day,
the fellow got his tape,
And murmured as he started putting it
around her shape:**

Chorus

**"You've got a long way to go,
you've got a long way to go;
Oh what a terrible lump of stuff,
The three-yard measure ain't large enough;
She's over ninety-five round her "Seraglio,"
To find a pair of pants to fit her,
you've got a long way to go." ▶**

Verse 2
Once on a donkey's back,
I tried Dick Turpin's ride to York,
When suddenly the moke stopped dead and
I got off to walk.
'Twas miles out in the country and
he wouldn't move for me,
I asked a slop where London was,
"Lord luv a duck," said he:

Chorus
"You've got a long way to go, you've got a
long way to go."
He gave the Jerusalem moke a smack,
And planted a pin in its "Union Jack,"
He wouldn't move an inch, the copper said,
"What ho!
You'd better get hold of the donkey's rudder,
you've got a long way to go."

Verse 3
My wife ain't noted for her looks,
her chivvy chase, Oh lor!
It's like a Chinese puzzle or the knocker
on the door.
The kids all called her "Monkey Brand"
in our localitee,
To find out such a specimen of
phi-si-og-no-mee—

Chorus
You've got a long way to go, you've got
a long way to;
Talk of the girls at the Sandwich Isles
With warts and pimples all round their dials,
I've seen some ugly mugs on view
at Barnum's Show,
But to find a face like my old woman's,
you've got a long way to go.

Verse 4
One day I saw a lady friend a-marching
up the West
With such a goody, pious band in blue
and scarlet dressed;
She banged upon the tambourine, and
shouted to the lot,
"We're marching on to glory!", I said,
"Marching on to What?"

Chorus
You've got a long way to go, you've got
a long way to go;
It's no use banging your blooming drum,
And shouting "Sinners, Oh! Will you come!"
I like to hear you say you're going
to glory, Flo,
If you're only as far as Piccadilly,
you've got a long way to go.

Frank Coyne, born Josiah Jones, was a Music Hall performer who was to die in 1906 at the age of just 31. 'You've Got A Long Way To Go' was one of the best-known numbers of his short career but it has to be said that it is the sort of song that did little to change the minds of those who held the view that Music Hall was an essentially vulgar form of entertainment. That noted, the song by A.J. Mills and F.W. Carter, presents a different situation in each verse linking them with a chorus line common to each. Such songs are virtually jokes set to music, and they demand more art than may be at first apparent in tying together such disparate gags. Each situation is clearly and economically set forth although the topics generally go for low humour occasionally redeemed by a clever choice of word or phrase. Thus we hear of an impossibly fat daughter being measured for bloomers; a stubbornly immobile donkey; a 'celebration' of a wife's grotesquely ugly face; and a pious Salvation Army band bound for Glory. In each case the refrain is 'You've got a long way to go', a phrase that is variously adapted to the measurement of the daughter's formidable hips, a donkey ride terminated far short of its destination and so on. Delight in the ugly, which in the verse about a wife's face seems pointlessly offensive, was a common characteristic of the Music Hall. Perhaps that kind of humour was simply a wilful protest against conventional standards of beauty or perhaps it was just a perverse delight in the exceptionally unattractive, reversals and inversions often being found in Victorian and Edwardian entertainments. W. S. Gilbert might have done it more elegantly but he was no less a fan of the topsy-turvy plot device, a chronic source of annoyance to his partner Arthur Sullivan who saw it as a cliché over indulged. The song ends on a comparative high, last verse being a wry reminder that the spiritual is all very well but to those practical souls tethered to here and now, Salvation Army officers marching to Glory from the seamy purlieus of Piccadilly Circus might indeed find they to have a long way to go.

PROGRAMME

1 2 3 4 5 6 7 8 9